The Great Books Reading & Discussion Program

SECOND SERIES · VOLUME THREE

The Great Books Foundation

A Nonprofit Educational Corporation

Designed by Don Walkoe Design, Chicago

Handmade marbled paper, photographed on cover,
courtesy of Andrews, Nelson, Whitehead.

.

Published and distributed by

The Great Books Foundation
A Nonprofit Educational Corporation
40 East Huron Street
Chicago, Illinois 60611

Acknowledgments

"The Crito" by Plato from *Socrates and Legal Obligation*, translated by R. E. Allen. Copyright 1980 by the University of Minnesota. Reprinted by permission of the publisher, University of Minnesota Press.

"The Virtues" from *Ethics* in Volume 5 of *The Middle Works, 1899–1924* by John Dewey, edited by Jo Ann Boydston. Reprinted by permission of the publisher, Center for Dewey Studies, Southern Illinois University at Carbondale.

"Iphigeneia at Aulis" by Euripides, translated by W. S. Merwin and George E. Dimock, Jr. from *The Greek Tragedy in New Translations*, edited by William Arrowsmith. Copyright 1978 by W. S. Merwin and George E. Dimock, Jr. Reprinted by permission of the publisher, Oxford University Press, Inc.

"Notes from the Underground" from *Great Short Works of Fyodor Dostoevsky*, translated by David Magarshack. Published 1968 by Harper & Row, Publishers, Inc. Reprinted by permission of Mrs. Elsie D. Magarshack.

"Billy Budd, Sailor" from *Billy Budd, Sailor (An Inside Narrative)* by Herman Melville, edited by Harrison Hayford and Merton M. Sealts, Jr. Copyright 1962 by The University of Chicago. Reprinted by permission of the publisher, The University of Chicago Press.

"The Knight of Faith" from *Fear and Trembling; Repetition* by Søren Kierkegaard, translated and edited by Howard V. Hong and Edna H. Hong. Copyright 1983 by Howard V. Hong. Reprinted by permission of the publisher, Princeton University Press.

"The Persian Wars" from *Herodotus: The Histories*, Books VII and VIII, translated by Aubrey de Sélincourt. Copyright 1954 by the Estate of Aubrey de Sélincourt. Reprinted by permission of the publisher, Penguin Books, Ltd.

A source note appears, together with biographical information about the author, opposite the opening page of each work in this series. Footnotes by the author are not bracketed; footnotes by GBF or a translator are [bracketed].

CONTENTS

*

THE PERSIAN WARS
Herodotus / *Page 1*

.

OF CIVIL GOVERNMENT
John Locke / *Page 129*

.

GULLIVER'S TRAVELS
Jonathan Swift / *Page 161*

.

CIVIL DISOBEDIENCE
Henry David Thoreau / *Page 241*

HERODOTUS, often considered the "Father of History" for his pioneering efforts in that discipline, was born in about 484 B.C. in Halicarnassus, a dependency of Persia in Asia Minor. As a young man, Herodotus began a series of travels that took him through most of Asia Minor, Egypt, and Greece over a period of years. During his travels, Herodotus researched and prepared the *History,* his account of the Greco-Persian Wars. He may have lived in Athens for a time, and eventually settled in Thurii, an Athenian colony in the south of Italy. Herodotus died in about 425 B.C.

From *Herodotus: The Histories,* translated by Aubrey de Sélincourt. Publisher: Penguin Books, Ltd. 1983. Pages 441–575.

The Persian Wars

[In the preceding chapters of this work Herodotus traces the origins of the conflict between Greece and the East from the founding of the Persian Empire by Cyrus (550–529 B.C.) to the conquest of Egypt by Cambyses (529–521 B.C.). He then goes on to describe the consolidation and further expansion of the empire, both to the east and to the west toward Europe, under Darius (521–485 B.C.).

Having gained control of the Ionian Greek settlements along the Anatolian coast, Darius set up local tyrants to govern in his name. Outraged at the loss of their accustomed liberties, the Ionians rebelled (499 B.C.), calling upon the mainland Greeks for aid. Athens and the tiny Eretria alone responded to their plea, and the revolt was soon quelled—but not before the united Greek forces had sacked and burned the Lydian capital of Sardis.

According to Herodotus, this attack rankled Darius so bitterly that the punishment of Athens became a major Persian objective. In 490 B.C., Darius sent a force across the Aegean into Greece. Roused by their dynamic general Miltiades, the Athenians marched out to meet the Persians on the Plain of Marathon where they won a decisive victory over an army more than twice their size. The aim of the next, much larger, Persian expedition would be, not merely the punishment of Athens, but the conquest of Greece.

In the following selection (Books 7 and 8), Herodotus presents the culminating drama of his history—the invasion of Greece in 480–479 B.C. by Xerxes, son of Darius and ruler of the vast and powerful Persian Empire.]

1

BOOK SEVEN

When the news of the battle of Marathon reached Darius, son of Hystaspes and king of Persia, his anger against Athens, already great enough on account of the assault on Sardis, was even greater, and he was more than ever determined to make war on Greece. Without loss of time he dispatched couriers to the various states under his dominion with orders to raise an army much larger than before; and also warships, transports, horses, and grain. So the royal command went round; and all Asia was in an uproar for three years, with the best men being enrolled in the army for the invasion of Greece, and with the preparations. In the year after that, a rebellion in Egypt, which had been conquered by Cambyses, served only to harden Darius' resolve to go to war, not only against Greece but against Egypt too. . . .

Death, however, cut him off before his preparations were complete . . . , so [he] was robbed of his chance to punish either Egypt or the Athenians. After his death the crown passed to his son Xerxes.

Xerxes at first was not at all interested in invading Greece but began his reign by building up an army for a campaign in Egypt. But Mardonius—the son of Gobryas and Darius' sister and thus cousin to the king—who was present in court and had more influence with Xerxes than anyone else in the country, used constantly to talk to him on the subject. "Master," he would say, "the Athenians have done us great injury, and it is only right that they should be punished for their crimes. By all means finish the task you already have in hand; but when you have tamed the arrogance of Egypt, then lead an army against Athens. Do that, and your name will by held in honour all over the world, and people will think twice in future before they invade your country." And to the argument for revenge he would add that Europe was a very beautiful place; it produced every kind of garden tree; the land there was everything that land should be—it was, in short, too good for anyone in the world except the Persian king. Mardonius' motive for urging the campaign was love of mischief and adventure and the hope of becoming governor of Greece himself; and after much persistence he persuaded Xerxes to make the attempt. Certain other occurrences came to his aid. In the first place, messengers arrived from the Aleuadae in Thessaly (the Aleuadae were the Thessalian reigning family) with an invitation to Xerxes, promising zealous assistance; at the same time the Pisistratidae[1] in Susa spoke to the same purpose and worked upon him even more strongly through the agency of an Athenian named Onomacritus, a collector of oracles. . . . Whenever he found himself in the king's presence, the Pisistratidae would talk big about his wonderful powers and he would recite selections from his oracles. Any prophecy which implied a setback to the Persian cause he would carefully omit, choosing for quotation only those which promised the brightest triumphs, describing to Xerxes how it was foreordained that the Hellespont should be bridged by a Persian, and how the army would march from Asia into Greece. Subjected, therefore, to this double pressure, from Onomacritus' oracles on the one side, and the advice of the Pisistratidae and Aleuadae on the other, Xerxes gave in and allowed himself to be persuaded to undertake the invasion of Greece.

First, however, in the year after Darius' death, he sent an army against the Egyptian rebels and decisively crushed them; then, having reduced the country to a condition of worse servitude than it had ever been in in the previous reign, he turned it over to his brother Achaemenes. . . .

After the conquest of Egypt, when he was on the point of taking in hand the expedition against Athens, Xerxes called a conference of the leading men in the country, to find out their

---

[1] [Exiled from democratic Athens and living at the court in Susa, Hippias, son of the former tyrant of Athens, urged the Persians to attack his city and restore his clan, the Pisistratidae, to despotic power.]

The Invasion of Greece
by Xerxes, 480-479 B.C.

– – – – – – Route of the Persian Army

attitude towards the war and explain to them his own wishes. When they met, he addressed them as follows: "Do not suppose, gentlemen, that I am departing from precedent in the course of action I intend to undertake. We Persians have a way of living, which I have inherited from my predecessors and propose to follow. I have learned from my elders that ever since Cyrus deposed Astyages and we took over from the Medes the sovereign power we now possess, we have never yet remained inactive. This is God's guidance, and it is by following it that we have gained our great prosperity. Of our past history you need no reminder; for you know well enough the famous deeds of Cyrus, Cambyses, and my father Darius, and their additions to our empire. Now I myself, ever since my accession, have been thinking how not to fall short of the kings who have sat upon this throne before me, and how to add as much power as they did to the Persian empire. And now at last I have found a way to win for Persia not glory only but a country as large and as rich as our own—indeed richer than our own—and at the same time to get satisfaction and revenge. That, then, is the object of this meeting—that I may disclose to you what it is that I intend to do. I will bridge the Hellespont and march an army through Europe into Greece, and punish the Athenians for the outrage they committed upon my father and upon us. As you saw, Darius himself was making his preparations for war against these men; but death prevented him from carrying out his purpose. I therefore on his behalf, and for the benefit of all my subjects, will not rest until I have taken Athens and burnt it to the ground, in revenge for the injury which the Athenians without provocation once did to me and my father. These men, you remember, came to Sardis with Aristagoras the Milesian, a subject of ours, and burnt the temples and sacred groves; and you know all too well how they served our troops under Datis and Artaphernes, when they landed upon Greek soil. For these reasons

I have now prepared to make war upon them, and, when I consider the matter, I find several advantages in the venture; if we crush the Athenians and their neighbours in the Peloponnese, we shall so extend the empire of Persia that its boundaries will be God's own sky, so that the sun will not look down upon any land beyond the boundaries of what is ours. With your help I shall pass through Europe from end to end and make it all one country. For if what I am told is true, there is not a city or nation in the world which will be able to withstand us, once these are out of the way. Thus the guilty and the innocent alike shall bear the yoke of servitude.

"If, then, you wish to gain my favour, each one of you must present himself willingly and in good heart on the day which I shall name; whoever brings with him the best equipped body of troops I will reward with those marks of distinction held in greatest value by our countrymen. That is what you must do; but so that I shall not appear to consult only my own whim, I will throw the whole matter into open debate, and ask any of you who may wish to do so, to express his views."

The first to speak after the king was Mardonius. "Of all Persians who have ever lived," he began, "and of all who are yet to be born, you, my lord, are the greatest. Every word you have spoken is true and excellent, and you will not allow the wretched Ionians in Europe to make fools of us. It would indeed be an odd thing if we who have defeated and enslaved the Sacae, Indians, Ethiopians, Assyrians, and many other great nations for no fault of their own, but merely to extend the boundaries of our empire, should fail now to punish the Greeks who have been guilty of injuring us without provocation. Have we anything to fear from them? The size of their army? Their wealth? The question is absurd; we know how they fight; we know how slender their resources are. People of their race we have already reduced to subjection—I mean the Greeks of Asia, Ionians, Aeolians, and Dorians. I myself before now have had some experience of these men, when under orders from your father I invaded their country; and I got as far as Macedonia—indeed almost to Athens itself—without a single soldier daring to oppose me. Yet, from what I hear, the Greeks are pugnacious enough, and start fights on the spur of the moment without sense or judgement to justify them. When they declare war on each other, they go off together to the smoothest and levellest bit of ground they can find, and have their battle on it—with the result that even the victors never get off without heavy losses, and as for the losers—well, they're wiped out. Now surely, as they all talk the same language, they ought to be able to find a better way of settling their differences: by negotiation, for instance, or an interchange of views—indeed by anything rather than fighting. Or if it is really impossible to avoid coming to blows, they might at least employ the elements of strategy and look for a strong position to fight from. In any case, the Greeks, with their absurd notions of warfare, never even thought of opposing me when I led my army to Macedonia.

"Well then, my lord, who is likely to resist you when you march against them with the millions of Asia at your back, and the whole Persian fleet? Believe me, it is not in the Greek character to take so desperate a risk. But should I be wrong and they be so foolish as to do battle with us, then they will learn that we are the best soldiers in the world. Nevertheless, let us take this business seriously and spare no pains; success is never automatic in this world—nothing is achieved without trying."

Xerxes' proposals were made to sound plausible enough by these words of Mardonius, and when he stopped speaking there was a silence. For a while nobody dared to put forward the opposite view, until Artabanus, taking courage from the fact of his relationship to the king—he was a son of Hystaspes and therefore Xerxes' uncle—rose to speak "My lord," he said, "without a debate in which both sides of a question are expressed, it is not possible to choose the better course. All one can do is to accept whatever it is that has been proposed. But grant a debate, and there is a fair choice to be made. We cannot assess the purity of gold merely by looking at it: we test it by rubbing it on other gold—then we can tell which is the purer. I warned your father—Darius my own brother—not to attack the Scythians, those wanderers who live in a cityless land. But he would not listen to me. Confident in his power to subdue them he invaded their country, and before he came home again many fine soldiers who marched with him were dead. But you, my lord, mean to attack a nation greatly superior to the Scythians: a nation with the highest reputation for valour both on land and at sea. It is my duty to tell you what you have to fear from them: you have said you mean to bridge the Hellespont and march through Europe to Greece. Now suppose—and it is not impossible—that you were to suffer a reverse by sea or land, or even both. These Greeks are said to be great fighters—and indeed one might well guess as much from the fact that the Athenians alone destroyed the great army we sent to attack them under Datis and Artaphernes. Or, if you will, suppose they were to succeed upon one element only—suppose they fell upon our fleet and defeated it, and then sailed to the Hellespont and destroyed the bridge: then, my lord, you would indeed be in peril. It is no special wisdom of my own that makes me argue as I do; but just such a disaster as I have suggested did, in fact, very nearly overtake us when your father bridged the Thracian Bosphorus and the Danube to take his army into Scythia. You will remember how on that occasion the Scythians went to all lengths in their efforts to induce the Ionian guard to break the Danube bridge, and how Histiaeus, the lord of Miletus, merely by following the advice of the other Ionian despots instead of rejecting it, as he did, had it in his power to ruin Persia. Surely it is a dreadful thing even to hear said, that the fortunes of the king once wholly depended upon a single man.

"I urge you, therefore, to abandon this plan; take my advice and do not run any such terrible risk when there is no necessity to do so. Break up this conference; turn the matter over quietly by yourself, and then, when you think fit, announce your decision. Nothing is more valuable to a man than to lay his plans carefully and well; even if things go against him, and forces he cannot control bring his enterprise to nothing, he still has the satisfaction of knowing that it was not his fault—the plans were all laid; if, on the other hand, he leaps headlong into danger and succeeds by luck—well, that's a bit of luck indeed, but he still has the shame of knowing that he was ill prepared.

"You know, my lord, that amongst living creatures it is the great ones that God smites with his thunder, out of envy of their pride. The little ones do not vex him. It is always the great buildings and the tall trees which are struck by lightning. It is God's way to bring the lofty low. Often a great army is destroyed by a little one, when God in his envy puts fear into the men's hearts, or sends a thunderstorm, and they are cut to pieces in a way they do not deserve. For God tolerates pride in none but Himself. Haste is the mother of failure—and for failure we always pay a heavy price; it is in delay our profit lies—perhaps it may not immediately be apparent, but we shall find it, sure enough, as time goes on.

"This, my lord, is the advice I offer you. And as for you, Mardonius, I warn you that the Greeks in no way deserve disparagement; so say no more silly things about them. By slandering the Greeks you increase the king's eagerness to make war on them, and, as far as I can see, this is the very thing you yourself most passionately desire. Heaven forbid it should happen! Slander is a wicked thing: in a case of slander two parties do wrong and one suffers by it. The slanderer is guilty in that he speaks ill of a man behind his back; and the man who listens to him is guilty in that he takes his word without troubling to find out the truth. The slandered person suffers doubly—from the disparaging words of the one and from the belief of the other that he deserves the disparagement.

"Nevertheless, if there is no avoiding this campaign in Greece, I have one final proposal to make. Let the king stay here in Persia; and you and I will then stake our children on the issue, and you can start the venture with the men you want and as big an army as you please. And if the king prospers, as you say he will, then I consent that my sons should be killed, and myself with them; if my own prediction is fulfilled, let *your* sons forfeit their lives—and you too—if you ever get home.

"Maybe you will refuse this wager, and still persist in leading an army into Greece. In that case I venture a prophecy: the day will come when many a man left at home will hear the news that Mardonius has brought disaster upon Persia, and that his body lies a prey to dogs and birds somewhere in the country of the Athenians or the Spartans—if not upon the road thither. For that is the way you will find out the quality of the people against whom you are urging the king to make war."

Xerxes was exceedingly angry. "Artabanus," he replied, "you are my father's brother, and that alone saves you from paying the price your empty and ridiculous speech deserves. But your cowardice and lack of spirit shall not escape disgrace: I forbid you to accompany me on my march to Greece—you shall stay at home with the women, and everything I spoke of I shall accomplish without help from you. If I fail to punish the Athenians, let me be no child of Darius, the son of Hystaspes, the son of Arsames, the son of Ariaramnes, the son of Teispes, the son of Cyrus, the son of Cambyses, the son of Teispes, the son of Achaemenes! I know too well that if we make no move, the Athenians will—they will be sure to invade our country. One has but to make the inference from what they did before; for it was they who marched into Asia and burnt Sardis. Retreat is no longer possible for either of us: if we do not inflict the wound, we shall assuredly receive it. All we possess will pass to the Greeks, or all they possess will pass to us. That is the choice before us; for in the enmity between us there is no middle course. It is right, therefore, that we should now revenge ourselves for the injury we once received; and no doubt in doing so I shall learn the nature of this terrible thing which is to happen to me, if I march against men whom Pelops the Phrygian, a mere slave of the Persian kings, once beat so soundly that to this very day both people and country bear the conqueror's name."

So ended the speeches at the conference. Later on that evening Xerxes began to be worried by what Artabanus had said, and during the night, as he turned it over in his mind, he came to the conclusion that the invasion of Greece would not, after all, be a good thing. Having reached this decision he fell asleep; and the Persians say that before the night was over he dreamed that the figure of a man, tall and of noble aspect, stood by his bed. "Lord of Persia," the phantom said, "have you changed your mind and decided not to lead an army against Greece, in spite of your proclamation to your subjects that troops should be raised? You are wrong to change; and there is one here who will not forgive you for doing so. Continue to tread the path which you chose yesterday." The visionary figure then flew away, and next morning Xerxes put the dream out of his mind and summoned a meeting of the same people as before. "Gentlemen," he said to them, "I ask your forbearance for changing my mind so quickly. My understanding has hardly yet grown to its full strength, and those who would force me into this war do not leave me alone for a moment. When I heard what Artabanus said, my hot young blood boiled up for the moment, and I flung some words at him such as a young man ought not to address to his senior. But now I acknowledge the justice of what he said, and I will take his advice. I have changed my mind; there will be no war against Greece. Peace is to continue."

The Persians were delighted at this, and bowed low before their master; but the following night Xerxes dreamed that the same figure as before stood by his bed and spoke to him. "Son of Darius," it said, "so you have openly, in the presence of your subjects, renounced the campaign and made light of what I said to you, as if it had never been said at all. Now let me tell you what the result will be, if you do not at once undertake this war: just as in a moment you rose to greatness and power so in a moment will you be brought low again."

Terrified by the dream Xerxes leapt out of bed and sent for Artabanus. "Artabanus," he said, "when you first gave me your good advice, I lost control of myself and answered wildly and foolishly. But I soon thought better of it and realized that I ought to do as you suggested. Now, however, I cannot do so, much as I should like it; for since I changed my mind I have been haunted by a dream which will not allow me to act as you advised. The last time I saw the vision, it left me with threats of disaster. Now if God sent the dream, and it is God's pleasure that we should invade Greece, the same vision will appear to you and will give you the same commands as it gave to me. And this, I think, is most likely to happen if you put on my clothes, take your seat on my throne, and then go to sleep in my bed."

Artabanus, who thought it was improper for him to sit on the royal throne, did not at once do as Xerxes bade; but at last he was forced to yield—though not until he had addressed Xerxes in the following words: "In my belief, my lord, readiness to listen to good advice comes to much the same thing as being wise oneself. You of course have both virtues; but you are led astray by the companionship of bad men. Their advice to you is like the gales of wind which do not allow the sea to be what it is meant to be—the thing, namely, in all the world most useful to us. As for myself, I was not so much hurt by your abuse of me as by the fact that when we were offered a choice between two courses, of which one tended to flatter our arrogance and the other to check it by pointing out how wrong it is to teach the heart always to seek for more than it possesses, you chose the one which is the more likely to lead both yourself and your country to disaster. Now you lean toward the better course; but you tell me that since you gave up your intention of attacking Greece, you have been haunted by a dream which will not let you lay your purpose aside. You imagine, my son, that your dream was sent by some god or other; but dreams do not come from God. I, who am older than you by many years, will tell you what these visions are that float before our eyes in sleep: nearly always these drifting phantoms are the shadows of what we have been thinking about during the day; and during the days before your dream we were, you know, very much occupied with this campaign. Nevertheless it is possible that your dream cannot be explained as I have explained it: perhaps there is, indeed, something divine in it—in which case what you have said sums the matter up completely: let it appear to me as well as to you, with its commands.

"All the same, if it means to come at all, it should not be more likely to come if I wear your clothes than if I wear my own, or if I sleep in your bed than if I sleep in mine. For surely this phantom of your dreams, whatever it may be, is not so foolish as to think that I am you simply because I wear your clothes. But, apart altogether from the question of clothes, should the phantom ignore me and not think fit to appear, but should nevertheless come again to you—well, that indeed is something we must take note of! For if it visits you often, even I shall admit that it is sent by God.

"As for the rest, if your mind is made up and I cannot turn you from your purpose: if I really must sleep in your bed—so be it. I will do what you command—and then let us see if the phantom comes. But until it does, I shall keep my own opinion on the matter."

Then Artabanus, hoping to prove that Xerxes was mistaken, did as he had been bidden. He dressed himself in the king's clothes and took his seat upon the royal throne; and afterwards when he had gone to bed and fallen asleep, he dreamt that the very same figure which had twice visited the king stood over him. "Are you the man," said the phantom, "who in would-be concern for the king is trying to dissuade him from making war on Greece? You will not escape unpunished, either now or hereafter, for seeking to turn aside the course of destiny; and as for Xerxes, he has been told already what will happen to him if he disobeys me." The phantom after uttering these threats was on the point of burning out Artabanus' eyes with hot irons, when he leapt up with a shriek, and ran to find Xerxes. Then, sitting beside him, he recounted the dream in detail and went on to speak in the following words: "Sire, like other men I have seen in my time powerful kingdoms struck down by weaker ones, and it was for that reason I tried to prevent you from giving way to the hot blood of youth. There is danger in insatiable desire, and I could not but remember the fate of Cyrus' campaign against the Massagetae and Cambyses' invasion of Ethiopia. Yes, and did I not march with Darius, too, against the Scythians? My memory of those disasters forced me to believe that the world would call you happy only if you lived in peace. But now I know that God is at work in this matter; and since apparently heaven itself is about to send ruin upon Greece, I admit that I was mistaken. Tell the Persians about the vision which God has sent us; make them prepare for war according to the orders which you previously gave them, and, as God is offering you this great opportunity, play your own part to the full in realizing it."

Both Artabanus and Xerxes now placed the fullest confidence in the dream. The king, at the first light of dawn, laid the whole matter before the Persians, and Artabanus who had been the only one openly to oppose the project of war, now no less openly supported it.

After Xerxes had made his decision to fight, he had a third dream. The Magi were consulted about its significance and expressed the opinion that it portended the conquest of the world and its total subjection to Persia. In the dream, Xerxes had imagined himself crowned with olive, of which the branches spread all over the earth; then the crown had suddenly vanished from his head. After the Magi's favourable interpretation, all the Persian nobles who had attended the conference hurried home to their respective provinces; and as every one of them hoped to win the reward which Xerxes had offered, no pains were spared in the subsequent preparations, and Xerxes, in the process of assembling his armies, had every corner of the continent ransacked. For the four years following the conquest of Egypt the mustering of troops and the provision of stores and equipment continued, and towards the close of the fifth Xerxes, at the head of his enormous force, began his march.

The army was indeed far greater than any other in recorded history. . . . There was not a nation in Asia that he did not take with him against Greece; save for the great rivers there was not a stream his army drank from that was not drunk dry. Some nations provided ships, others formed infantry units; from some cavalry was requisitioned, from others horse-transports and crews; from others, again, warships for floating bridges, or provisions and naval craft of various kinds.

In view of the previous disaster to the fleet off Mt. Athos, preparations had been going on in that area for the past three years. A fleet of triremes lay at Elaeus in the Chersonese, and from this base men of the various nations of which the army was composed were sent over in shifts to Athos, where they were put to the work of cutting a canal under the lash. The natives of Athos also took part. . . .

Mt. Athos is a high and famous mountain running out into the sea. People live on it, and where the high land ends on the landward side it forms a sort of isthmus with a neck about a mile and a half wide, all of which is level ground or low hillocks, across from the sea by Acanthus to the sea facing Torone. On this isthmus where Athos peters out stands the Greek town of Sane, and south of it, on Athos itself, are Dium, Olophyxus, Acrothoon, Thyssus, and Cleonae—the inhabitants of which Xerxes now proposed to turn into islanders.

I will now describe how the canal was cut. The ground was divided into sections for the men of the various nations, on a line taped across the isthmus from Sane. When the trench reached a certain depth, the labourers at the bottom carried on with the digging and passed the soil up to others above them, who stood on terraces and passed it on to another lot, still higher up, until it reached the men at the top, who carried it away and dumped it. . . . In a meadow nearby the workmen had their meeting-place and market, and grain ready ground was brought over in great quantity from Asia.

Thinking it over I cannot but conclude that it was mere ostentation that made Xerxes have the canal dug—he wanted to show his power and to leave something to be remembered by. There would have been no difficulty at all in getting the ships hauled across the isthmus on land; yet he ordered the construction of a channel for the sea broad enough for two warships to be rowed abreast. The same people who had to cut the canal also had orders to bridge the river Strymon. At the same time other work, too, was in progress: cables, some of papyrus, some of white flax, were being prepared for the bridges—a task which Xerxes entrusted to the Phoenicians and Egyptians; and provision dumps were being formed for the troops, lest either men or animals should go hungry on the march to Greece. For these dumps the most convenient sites were chosen after a careful survey, the provisions being brought from many different parts of Asia in merchantmen or transport vessels. The greatest quantity was collected at a place called the White Cape in Thrace. . . .

So the work went on, and meanwhile the great army—all the troops from the continent which were to take part in the expedition—had assembled according to orders at Critalla in Cappadocia, and from there began to move forward with Xerxes to Sardis. . . .

After crossing the Halys the army passed [on] to Celaenae. . . . Here at Celaenae a Lydian named Pythius, the son of Atys, was awaiting Xerxes, and on his arrival entertained him and the whole army with most lavish hospitality, and promised besides to furnish money for the expenses of the war. The mention of money caused Xerxes to ask the Persians present who Pythius was and if he was really rich enough to make such an offer. "My lord," was the answer, "it was this man who gave your father Darius the golden plane-tree and the golden vine; and still, so far as we know, he is the wealthiest man in the world, after yourself."

Xerxes was surprised by this latter statement, and repeated his question, this time asking Pythius himself how much money he possessed. "Sire," said Pythius, "I will be open with you and not pretend that I do not know the amount of my fortune. I do know it, and I will tell you exactly what it is. When I learned that you were on your way to the Aegean coast, my immediate wish was to make a contribution towards the expenses of the war; so I went into the matter of my finances and found upon calculation that I possessed 2000 talents of silver, and 3,993,000 gold Darics. This it is my intention to give you; I can live quite comfortably myself on my slaves and the produce of my estates."

Xerxes was much pleased. "My Lydian friend," he replied, "you are the only man I have met since I left Persian territory who has been willing to entertain my army, and nobody but you has come into my presence with an offer to contribute money for the war of his own free will. But you have done both, and on a magnificent scale. Therefore, as a reward for your generosity, I make you my personal friend and, in addition, I will give you from my own coffers 7000 gold Darics which are needed to make your fortune up to the round sum of 4,000,000. Continue, then, to possess what you have acquired; and have the wisdom to remain always the man you have proved yourself to-day. You will never regret it, now or hereafter."

Having carried out this promise, Xerxes moved on . . . , [heading for Sardis, the capital of Lydia.]

In Sardis, Xerxes' first act was to send representatives to every place in Greece except Athens and Sparta with a demand for earth and water and a further order to prepare entertainment for him against his coming. This renewed demand for submission was due to his confident belief that the Greeks who had previously refused to comply with the demand of Darius would now be frightened into complying with his own. It was to prove whether or not he was right that he took this step.

He then prepared to move forward to Abydos, where a bridge had already been constructed across the Hellespont from Asia to Europe. Between Sestos and Madytus in the Chersonese there is a rocky headland running out into the water opposite Abydos. It was here not long afterwards that the Greeks under Xanthippus the son of Ariphron took Artaÿctes the Persian governor of Sestos, and nailed him alive to a plank—he was the man who collected women in the temple of Protesilaus at Elaeus and committed various acts of sacrilege. This headland was the point to which Xerxes' engineers carried their two bridges from Abydos—a distance of seven furlongs. One was constructed by the Phoenicians using flax cables, the other by the Egyptians with papyrus cables. The work was successfully completed, but a subsequent storm of great violence smashed it up and carried everything away. Xerxes was very angry when he learned of the disaster, and gave orders that the Hellespont should receive three hundred lashes and have a pair of fetters thrown into it. I have heard before now that he also sent people to brand it with hot irons. He certainly instructed the men with the whips to utter, as they wielded them, the barbarous and presumptuous words:

"You salt and bitter stream, your master lays this punishment upon you for injuring him, who never injured you. But Xerxes the King will cross you, with or without your permission. No man sacrifices to you, and you deserve the neglect by your acid and muddy waters." In addition to punishing the Hellespont, Xerxes gave orders that the men responsible for building the bridges should have their heads cut off. The men who received these invidious orders duly carried them out, and other engineers completed the work. The method employed was as follows: galleys and triremes were lashed together to support the bridges—360 vessels for the one on the Black Sea side, and 314 for the other. They were moored slantwise to the Black Sea and at right angles to the Hellespont, in order to lessen the strain on the cables. Specially heavy anchors were laid out both up-stream and downstream—those to the eastward to hold the vessels against winds blowing down the straits from the direction of the Black Sea, those on the other side, to the westward and towards the Aegean, to take the strain when it blew from the west and south. Gaps were left in three places to allow any boats that might wish to do so to pass in or out of the Black Sea.

Once the vessels were in position, the cables were hauled taut by wooden winches ashore. This time the two sorts of cable were not used separately for each bridge, but both bridges had two flax cables and four papyrus ones. The flax and papyrus cables were of the same thickness and quality, but the flax was the heavier—half a fathom of it weighed 114 lb. The next operation was to cut planks equal in length to the width of the floats, lay them edge to edge over the taut cables, and then bind them together on their upper surface. That done, brushwood was put on top and spread evenly, with a layer of soil, trodden hard, over all. Finally a paling was constructed along each side, high enough to prevent horses and mules from seeing over and taking fright at the water.

The bridges were now ready; and when news came from Athos that work on the canal was finished, including the breakwaters at its two ends, which had been built to prevent the surf from silting up the entrances, the army, after wintering at Sardis and completing its preparations, started the following spring on its march to Abydos.

No sooner had the troops begun to move than the sun vanished from his place in the sky and it grew dark as night, though the weather was perfectly clear and cloudless. Xerxes, deeply troubled, asked the Magi to interpret the significance of this strange phenomenon, and was given to understand that God meant to foretell to the Greeks the eclipse of their cities—for it was the sun which gave warning of the future to Greece, just as the moon did to Persia. Having heard this, Xerxes continued the march in high spirits.

The army, however, had not gone far when Pythius the Lydian, in alarm at the sign from heaven, was emboldened by the presents he had received to come to Xerxes with a request. "Master," he said, "there is a favour I should like you to grant me—a small thing, indeed, for you to perform, but to me of great importance, should you consent to do so." Xerxes, who thought the request would be almost anything but what it actually turned out to be, agreed to grant it and told Pythius to say what it was he wanted. This generous answer raised Pythius' hopes, and he said, "My lord, I have five sons, and it happens that every one of them is serving in your army in the campaign against Greece. I am an old man, Sire, and I beg you in pity to release from service one of my sons—the eldest—to take care of me and my property. Take the other four—and may you return with your purpose accomplished."

Xerxes was furiously angry. "You miserable fellow," he cried, "have you the face to mention your son, when I, in person, am marching to the war against Greece with my sons and brothers and kinsmen and friends—*you,* my slave, whose duty it was to come with me with every member of your house, including your wife? Mark my words: it is through the ears you can touch a man to pleasure or rage—let the spirit which dwells there hear good things, and it will fill the body with delight; let it hear bad, and it will swell with fury. When you did me good service, and offered more, you cannot boast that you were more generous than I; and now your punishment will be less than your impudence deserves. Yourself and four of your sons are saved by the entertainment you gave me; but you shall pay with the life of the fifth, whom you cling to most."

Having answered Pythius in these words, Xerxes at once gave orders that the men to whom such duties fell should find Pythius' eldest son and cut him in half and put the two halves one on each side of the road, for the army to march out between them. The order was performed.

And now between the halves of the young man's body the advance of the army began: first came the men with the gear and equipment, driving the pack-animals, and behind these a host of troops of all nationalities indiscriminately mixed. When more than half the army had passed, a gap was left in the marching column to keep these troops from contact with the king, who was immediately preceded by a thousand horsemen, picked out of all Persia, followed by a thousand similarly picked spearmen with spears reversed. Then came ten of the sacred horses, known as Nisaean, in magnificent harness. . . . They were followed by the holy chariot of Zeus drawn by eight white horses, with a charioteer on foot behind them holding the reins—for no mortal man may mount into that chariot's seat. Then came the king himself, riding in a chariot drawn by Nisaean horses, his charioteer, Patiramphes, son of Otanes the Persian, standing by his side.

That was how Xerxes rode from Sardis—and, when the fancy took him, he would leave his chariot and take his seat in a covered carriage instead. Behind him marched a thousand spearmen, their weapons pointing upwards in the usual way—all men of the best and noblest Persian blood; then a thousand picked

Persian cavalry, then—again chosen for quality out of all that remained—a body of Persian infantry ten thousand strong. . . . The ten thousand infantry were followed by a squadron of ten thousand Persian horses, after which there was a gap of two furlongs, and then came the remainder of the army, in a miscellaneous mass.

From Lydia the army made for . . . Mysia and thence proceeded . . . to Carene; then crossing the level country near Thebe, with Mt. Ida on its left [it] entered Trojan territory. During a night in camp at the foot of Mt. Ida a heavy storm of thunder and lightning caused the death of a considerable number of men. When the army reached the Scamander, the first river since the march from Sardis began, which failed to provide enough water for men and beasts, Xerxes had a strong desire to see Troy, the ancient city of Priam. Accordingly he went up into the citadel, and when he had seen what he wanted to see and heard the story of the place from the people there, he sacrificed a thousand oxen to the Trojan Athene, and the Magi made libations of wine to the spirits of the great men of old. During the night which followed there was panic in the camp. At dawn the march continued . . . [towards] Abydos.

Xerxes now decided to hold a review of his army. On a rise of ground nearby, a throne of white marble had already been specially prepared for his use by the people of Abydos; so the king took his seat upon it and, looking down over the shore, was able to see the whole of his army and navy at a single view. As he watched them he was seized with the desire to witness a rowing-match. The match took place and was won by the Phoenicians of Sidon, to the great delight of Xerxes who was as pleased with the race as with his army. And when he saw the whole Hellespont hidden by ships, and all the beaches and plains of Abydos filled with men, he congratulated himself— and the moment after burst into tears. Artabanus his uncle, the man who in the first instance had spoken his mind so freely in trying to dissuade Xerxes from undertaking the campaign, was by his side; and when he saw how Xerxes wept, he said to him; "My lord, surely there is a strange contradiction in what you do now and what you did a moment ago. Then you called yourself a lucky man—and now you weep."

"I was thinking," Xerxes replied; "and it came into my mind how pitifully short human life is—for of all these thousands of men not one will be alive in a hundred years' time."

"Yet," said Artabanus, "there are sadder things in life even than that. Short as it is, there is not a man in the world, either here or elsewhere, who is happy enough not to wish—not once only but again and again—to be dead rather than alive. Troubles come, diseases afflict us; and this makes life, despite its brevity, seem all too long. So heavy is the burden of it that death is a refuge which we all desire, and it is common proof amongst us that God who gave us a taste of this world's sweetness has been a niggard in his giving."

"Artabanus," Xerxes replied, "the lot of men here upon earth is indeed as you have described it; but let us put aside these gloomy reflections, for we have pleasant things in hand. Now tell me—if that figure had not appeared to you so vividly in your dream, would you have clung to your original opinion and tried to prevent me from making war on Greece, or would you have changed your mind? Answer me truly."

"Sire," said Artabanus, "I pray that the dream we had may not disappoint either my hopes or your own. But ever since that night I have been beside myself with dread; many things contribute to the cause of it, but nothing so much as my knowledge that the two mightiest powers in the world are against you."

"What a strange man you are," said Xerxes; "tell me, what powers do you mean? Have you any fault to find with my army? Isn't it big enough? Do you think the Greek army will be several times as large, or our navy smaller than theirs? Which are you afraid of? Both perhaps! But if you feel that our force is inadequate, another army could easily be mustered with little delay."

"No man of sense, my lord," Artabanus answered, "could find any fault with the size of your army or the number of your ships. If you increase your forces, the two powers I have in mind will be even worse enemies to you than they are now. I will tell you what they are—the land and the sea. So far as I know there is not a harbour anywhere big enough to receive this fleet of ours and give it protection in the event of storms: and indeed there would have to be not merely one such harbour, but many—all along the coast by which you will sail. But there is not a single one; so I would have you realize, my lord, that men are at the mercy of circumstance, and not their master.

"Now let me tell you of your other great enemy, the land. If you meet with no opposition, the land itself will become more and more hostile to you the further you advance, drawn on and on; for men are never satisfied by success. What I mean is this—if nobody stops your advance, the land itself—the mere distance growing greater and greater as the days go by—will ultimately starve you. No: the best man, in my belief, is he who lays his plans warily, with an eye for every disaster which might occur, and then, when the time comes, acts boldly."

"There is good sense," Xerxes answered, "in everything you have said; nevertheless you ought not to be so timid always, or to think of every accident which might possibly overtake us. If upon the proposal of a plan you were always to weigh equally all possible chances, you would never do anything. I would much rather take a risk and run into trouble half the time than keep out of any trouble through being afraid of everything.

"If you dispute whatever is said to you, but can never prove your objections, you are as likely to be wrong as the other man—indeed there is nothing to choose between you. And as for proof—how can a man ever be certain? Certainty, surely, is beyond human grasp. But however that may be, the usual thing is that profit comes to those who are willing to act, not to the overcautious and hesitant. Just think how the power of Persia has grown: if my predecessors had felt as you do—or even if they had not, but had taken the advice of men who did—you would never have seen our country in its present glory. No indeed: it was by taking risks that my ancestors brought us to where we stand to-day. Only by great risks can great results be achieved. We, therefore, are following in the footsteps of our fathers; we are marching to war at the best season of the year; we shall conquer all Europe, and—without being starved to death anywhere or having any other unpleasant experience—we shall return home in triumph. For one thing, we are carrying ample stores with us; for another, we will have the grain belonging to any country we may enter, no matter who lives there. Our enemies, remember, are not nomad tribes—they are agricultural peoples."

"Sire," said Artabanus, "though you will not listen to my fears, take, at least, one piece of advice from me—for when there is much to talk of, many words are needed. Cyrus, the son of Cambyses, conquered and made tributary to Persia all Ionia except Athens; I urge you therefore on no account to take these Ionians to attack men of their own blood. We are well able to defeat our enemy without their help. If the Ionians come with us, they will have two courses open to them: either to prove themselves scoundrels by helping to enslave their mother country, or to prove themselves honest men by helping to keep her free. By choosing the former course they will do us little good; by choosing the latter they will be able to cause serious injury to your army. Remember, I beg you, the truth of the old saying, that the end is not always to be seen in the beginning."

Xerxes answered: "Artabanus, of all the views you have put forward you are most mistaken in your fear that the Ionians will desert our cause. We have the best possible proof of their reliability, and you yourself like everybody else who took part in Darius' Scythian campaign can bear witness to it. On that occasion, when the Ionians had it in their power to save or destroy the whole Persian army, they did us no harm but acted with loyalty and honour. Besides, there is another reason for trusting them: for is it conceivable that they will try to wreck our cause, when they have left their wives, children, and property in our country? You may, therefore, dismiss this fear from your mind. Doubt nothing, and keep safe for me my house and dominions; for to you, and you alone, I give my sovereignty in trust."

After this conversation Xerxes sent Artabanus back to Susa and then summoned a meeting of the leading Persians. "Gentlemen," he said to them, "I have brought you here because I wished to ask you to show courage in what lies before us; you must not disgrace our countrymen, who in former days did so much that was great and admirable. Let each and all of us exert ourselves to the utmost; for the noble aim we are striving to achieve concerns every one of us alike. Fight this war with all your might—and for this reason: our enemies, if what I hear is true, are brave men, and if we defeat them, there is no other army in the world which will ever stand up to us again. And now let us pray to the gods who have our country in their keeping—and cross the bridge."

All that day the preparations for the crossing continued; and on the following day, while they waited for the sun which they wished to see as it rose, they burned all sorts of spices on the bridges and laid boughs of myrtle along the way. Then sunrise came, and Xerxes poured wine into the sea out of a golden goblet and, with his face turned to the sun, prayed that no chance might prevent him from conquering Europe or turn him back before he reached its utmost limits. His prayer ended, he flung the cup into the Hellespont and with it a golden bowl and a Persian *acinaces,* or short sword. I cannot say for certain if he intended the things which he threw into the water to be an offering to the Sun-god; perhaps they were—or it may be that they were a gift to the Hellespont itself, to show he was sorry for having caused it to be lashed with whips. . . .

From the European shore Xerxes watched his troops coming over under the whips. The crossing occupied seven days and nights without a break. There is a story that some time after Xerxes had passed the bridge, a native of the country thereabouts exclaimed: "Why, O God, have you assumed the shape of a man of Persia, and changed your name to Xerxes, in order to lead everyone in the world to the conquest and devastation of Greece? You could have destroyed Greece without going to that trouble."

After the whole army had reached the European shore and the forward march had begun, an extraordinary thing occurred—a mare gave birth to a hare. Xerxes paid no attention to this omen, though the significance of it was easy enough to understand. Clearly it meant that he was to lead an army against Greece with the greatest pomp and circumstance, and then to come running for his life back to the place he started from. There had previously been another strange and ominous occurrence in Sardis, when a mule dropped a foal with a double set of sexual organs, male and female—the former uppermost. Xerxes, however, ignored both omens and continued his march at the head of the army. The fleet followed the coast in a westerly direction down the Hellespont and then on to Cape Sarpedon, where it had orders to wait, and thus started in the opposite direction to the army, which marched eastwards through the Chersonese. . . . After passing through a place called The Market, it skirted the Black Gulf and crossed the river which gives the gulf its name. . . . From that point it turned west . . . [for] Doriscus.

Doriscus is the name given to a strip of coast in Thrace backed by a large plain through which flows the large river Hebrus. A fortress—also called Doriscus—had been built here, and a Persian

garrison left in it by Darius ever since his invasion of Scythia. . . .
Here the ships were all hauled ashore and allowed to dry out.

Meanwhile Xerxes at Doriscus was occupied in numbering
his troops. As nobody has left a record, I cannot state the precise
number of men provided by each separate nation, but the grand
total, excluding the naval contingent, turned out to be 1,700,000.
The counting was done by first packing ten thousand men as
close together as they could stand and drawing a circle round
them on the ground; they were then dismissed, and a fence,
about navel-high, was constructed round the circle; finally other
troops were marched into the area thus enclosed and dismissed
in their turn, until the whole army had been counted. After the
counting, the army was reorganized in divisions according to
nationality.

The nations of which the army was composed were as follows.
First the Persians themselves: the dress of these troops consisted
of the tiara, or soft felt cap, embroidered tunic with sleeves, a
coat of mail looking like the scales of a fish, and trousers; for
arms they carried light wicker shields, quivers slung below them,
short spears, powerful bows with cane arrows, and daggers
swinging from belts beside the right thigh. They were commanded by Otanes, the father of Xerxes' wife, Amestris. In
ancient times the Greek name for the Persians was Cephenes,
though they were known to themselves and their neighbours as
Artaei. It was not till Perseus, the son of Zeus and Danae, on
a visit to Cepheus, the son of Belus, married his daughter Andromeda and had by her a son whom he named Perses (and
left behind in that country because Cepheus had no male heir)
that the Persians took, from this Perses, their present name. . . .

[Herodotus here provides a detailed description of the troops sent by
the various nations under Persian control. These include Medes, Assyrians, Indians, Scythians, Caspians, Thracians, Ethiopians, Arabs,
and many more.]

Such, then, were the troops of the various nations which made up the infantry. The names of their chief commanders I have already recorded; it was they who organized and numbered the troops, and appointed the commanders of thousands and myriads of men. The latter were responsible for appointing men to take charge of small units—squads of ten or a hundred. There were also other officers commanding contingents and nations, but those whom I mentioned above were the commanders.

Over them, and in general command of the infantry, were Mardonius, the son of Gobryas, Tritantaechmes, the son of Artabanus (the man who voted against the campaign), Smerdomenes, the son of Otanes (both nephews of Darius and Xerxes' cousins), Masistes, the son of Darius and Atossa, Gergis, the son of Ariazus, and Megabyzus, the son of Zopyrus. These six commanded all the infantry except the Ten Thousand—a body of picked Persian troops under the leadership of Hydarnes, the son of Hydarnes. This corps was known as the Immortals, because it was invariably kept up to strength; if a man was killed or fell sick, the vacancy he left was at once filled, so that its strength was never more nor less than 10,000.

Of all the troops in the army the native Persians were not only the best but also the most magnificently equipped; their dress and armour I have mentioned already, but should add that every man glittered with the gold which he carried about his person in unlimited quantity. They were accompanied, moreover, by covered carriages containing their women and servants, all elaborately fitted out. Special food, separate from that of the rest of the army, was brought along for them on camels and mules.

The nations above mentioned use cavalry, but for this expedition only the following provided it: first the Persians—armed in the same way as their infantry, except that some of them wore devices of hammered bronze or iron on their heads. Secondly, a nomad tribe called Sagartians, a people who speak

Persian and dress in a manner half Persian, half Pactyan: these furnished a contingent 8000 strong. Their custom is to carry no weapons of bronze or iron except daggers; the special weapon upon which they chiefly rely is the lasso made of plaited strips of hide. In action, the moment they are in contact with the enemy, they throw their lassos, which have a noose at the end, and haul towards them whatever they catch, horse or man. The victim, tied up and helpless, is then dispatched. The Sagartian contingent was attached to the Persian. The Medes and Cissians were equipped like their infantry. The Indians, also armed like the Indian foot, rode, some on horseback, some in chariots drawn by either horses or wild asses. The Bactrians and Caspians were equipped like their infantry. The Libyans were like their infantry in equipment, but all riding in chariots. The Caspeirians and Paricanians again had the same arms as their infantry. The Arabians, equipped like their infantry, rode camels, which in speed are not inferior to horses.

These were the only nations which provided cavalry, and the total strength, not counting camels and chariots, was 80,000. The cavalry was drawn up in squadrons, and the Arabian contingent brought up the rear to avoid spreading panic amongst the horses, who cannot endure the presence of camels. In command of the cavalry were Datis' two sons, Harmamithras and Tithaeus. . . .

The fleet, apart from transport vessels, consisted of 1207 triremes. They were furnished as follows: (i) the Phoenicians, with the Syrians of Palestine, contributed 300. The crews wore helmets very like the Greek ones, and linen corslets; they were armed with rimless shields and javelins. These people have a tradition that in ancient times they lived on the Persian Gulf, but migrated to the Syrian coast, where they are found to-day. This part of Syria, together with the country which extends southward to Egypt, is all known as Palestine. . . .

[In like manner, Herodotus accounts for the naval contribution, the gear, and the dress of the various contingents of the Persian fleet.

Among those enlisted in the Persian cause are Ionian, Aeolian, and Hellespontian Greeks.]

All the ships also carried Persians, Medes, or Sacae as marines. The fastest ships were the Phoenician—and of these the Sidonian were the best. The men who served with the fleet, like those who served with the army, had their own native officers; but, as my story does not require it, I do not propose to mention their names. Some of them were far from distinguished, and every nation had as many officers as it had towns. In any case, these native officers were not really commanders; like the rest of the troops, they merely served under compulsion. The names of the Persian generals who had the real command and were at the head of the contingents sent by the various nations, I have already recorded. . . .

[Herodotus next gives the names of the Persian naval commanders and of the most renowned Persians aboard the fleet.]

There is no need for me to mention all the other subordinate officers, but there is one name which I cannot omit—that of Artemisia. It seems to me a most strange and interesting thing that she—a woman—should have taken part in the campaign against Greece. On the death of her husband the sovereign power had passed into her hands, and she sailed with the fleet in spite of the fact that she had a grown-up son and that there was consequently no necessity for her to do so. Her own spirit of adventure and manly courage were her only incentives. She was the daughter of Lygdamis, a Halicarnassian; on her mother's side she was Cretan. She sailed in command of the men of Halicarnassus, Cos, Nisyra, and Calydna, and furnished five ships of war. They were the most famous in the fleet, after the contingent from Sidon, and not one of the confederate commanders gave Xerxes sounder advice than she did. The places

I mentioned as being under her rule are all Dorian—the Halicarnassians being colonists from Troezen, and the rest from Epidaurus.

I have now finished what I had to say about the fleet.

When the counting and marshalling of the troops had been completed, Xerxes thought he would like to hold a general review. Accordingly he drove in his chariot past the contingents of all the various nations, asking questions, the answers to which were taken down by his secretaries, until he had gone from one end of the army to the other, both horse and foot. Next the ships were launched, and Xerxes dismounting from his chariot went aboard a Sidonian vessel, where he took his seat under a canopy of gold and sailed along the line of the anchored fleet, asking questions about each ship and having the answers recorded, just as he had done with the army. The ships' masters had taken their vessels some four hundred feet from the beach, and brought up there in a single line with the bows turned shoreward and the fighting men drawn up on deck fully armed as for war. To hold his review, Xerxes passed along between the line and the shore.

Having sailed from one end to the other of the line of anchored ships, Xerxes went ashore again and sent for Demaratus, the son of Ariston, who was accompanying him in the march to Greece. "Demaratus," he said, "it would give me pleasure at this point to put to you a few questions. You are a Greek, and a native, moreover, of by no means the meanest or weakest city in that country—as I learn not only from yourself but from the other Greeks I have spoken with. Tell me, then—will the Greeks dare to lift a hand against me? My own belief is that all the Greeks and all the other western peoples gathered together would be insufficient to withstand the attack of my army—and still more so if they are not united. But it is your opinion upon this subject that I should like to hear."

"My lord," Demaratus replied, "is it a true answer you would like, or merely an agreeable one?"

"Tell me the truth," said the king, "and I promise that you will not suffer by it." Encouraged by this Demaratus continued: "My lord, you bid me speak nothing but the truth, to say nothing which might later be proved a lie. Very well then; this is my answer: poverty is my country's inheritance from of old, but valour she won for herself by wisdom and the strength of law. By her valour Greece now keeps both poverty and bondage at bay.

"I think highly of all Greeks of the Dorian lands, but what I am about to say will apply not to all Dorians, but to the Spartans only. First then, they will not under any circumstances accept terms from you which would mean slavery for Greece; secondly, they will fight you even if the rest of Greece submits. Moreover, there is no use in asking if their numbers are adequate to enable them to do this; suppose a thousand of them take the field—then that thousand will fight you; and so will any number, greater than this or less."

Xerxes laughed. "My dear Demaratus," he exclaimed, "what an extraordinary thing to say! Do you really suppose a thousand men would fight an army like mine? Now tell me, would *you*, who were once, as you say, king of these people, be willing at this moment to fight ten men single-handed? I hardly think so; yet, if things in Sparta are really as you have described them, then, according to your laws, you as king ought to take on a double share—so that if every Spartan is a match for ten men of mine, I should expect you to be a match for twenty. Only in that way can you prove the truth of your claim. But if you Greeks, who think so much of yourselves, are all of the size and quality of those I have spoken with when they have visited my court—and of yourself, Demaratus—there is some danger of your words being nothing but an empty boast. But let me put my point as reasonably as I can—how is it possible that a thousand men, or ten thousand, or fifty thousand, should stand up to an army as big as mine, especially if they were not under a single master, but all perfectly free to do as they pleased? Suppose them to have five thousand men: in that case we should be more than a thousand to one! If, like ours, their troops were subject to the control of a single man, then possibly for fear of him, in spite of the disparity in numbers, they might show some sort of factitious courage, or let themselves be whipped into battle; but, as every man is free to follow his fancy, it is not conceivable that they should do either. Indeed, my own opinion is that even on equal terms the Greeks could hardly face the Persians alone. We, too, have this thing that you were speaking of—I do not say it is common, but it does exist; for instance, amongst the Persians in my bodyguard there are men who would willingly fight with three Greeks together. But you know nothing of such things, or you could not talk such non-sense."

"My lord," Demaratus answered, "I knew before I began that if I spoke the truth you would not like it. But, as you demanded the plain truth and nothing less, I told you how things are with the Spartans. Yet you are well aware that I now feel but little affection for my countrymen, who robbed me of my hereditary power and privileges and made me a fugitive without a home—whereas your father welcomed me at his court and gave me the means of livelihood and somewhere to live. Surely it is unreasonable to reject kindness; any sensible man will cherish it. Personally I do not claim to be able to fight ten men—or two; indeed I should prefer not even to fight with one. But should it be necessary—should there be some great cause to urge me on—then nothing would give me more pleasure than to stand up to one of those men of yours who claim to be a match for three Greeks. So it is with the Spartans; fighting singly, they are as good as any, but fighting together they are the best soldiers in the world. They are free—yes—but not entirely free; for they have a master, and that master is Law, which they fear much more than your subjects fear you. Whatever this master commands, they do; and his command never varies: it is never to retreat in battle, however great the odds, but always to stand firm, and to conquer or die. If, my lord, you think that what I have said is nonsense—very well; I am willing henceforward to hold my tongue. This time I spoke because you forced me to speak. In any case, I pray that all may turn out as you desire.''

Xerxes burst out laughing at Demaratus' answer, and good-humouredly let him go.

After the conversation I have recorded above, Xerxes appointed Mascames, son of Megadostes, to the governorship of Doriscus in place of the man who had been given that post by Darius, and then continued his march through Thrace towards Greece. Mascames was later to prove himself a very remarkable person; so much so, in fact, that Xerxes used to send a special present every year in recognition of his superiority to all the governors appointed either by himself or by Darius; moreover his son Artaxerxes showed the same favour to Mascames' descendants. Persian governors had held posts in Thrace and on the Hellespont before Xerxes' expedition, but in the years which succeeded it all of them except the governor of Doriscus were driven out by the Greeks—Mascames no one has yet been able to expel, though many have tried to do so. This is the reason for the annual present from the Persian king. . . .

From Doriscus Xerxes marched on towards Greece, pressing into his service the men of every nation which lay in his path; for . . . the whole country as far as Thessaly had been forced into subjection and made tributary to Persia. . . . After leaving Doriscus the army passed first by the Samothracian forts. . . .

[Keeping the Greek coastal settlements on his left, Xerxes marched westward through the territory of the Thracian tribes, all of which, except the Satrae, were forced to serve in the army.]

The Satrae, so far as one knows, have never yet been reduced to subjection, and are the only Thracian people to have kept their independence right down to the present day. The reason for this is the nature of their country, which consists of high mountains, thickly wooded with timber of all sorts and covered with snow. They are also first-rate fighters. It is in the territory of this people that there is an oracle of Dionysus, situated on the loftiest mountain range. The service of the temple belongs to the Bessi, a branch of the Satrae; and there is a Priestess, as at Delphi, to deliver the oracles—which, by the way, are not more involved than the Delphic. . . .

[Once through this region, Xerxes next passed the Pierian forts and the great mountain range of Pangaeum, continuing westward until he reached the town of Eion by the river Strymon.]

This latter river the Magi tried to propitiate by a sacrifice of white horses, and after performing many other magical tricks in the hope of winning the river's favour, they crossed it by the bridges which they found at Nine Ways, a place in the territory of the Edoni; and when they learned that Nine Ways was the name of the place, they took nine native boys and nine girls and buried them alive there. Burying people alive is a Persian custom; I understand that Xerxes' wife Amestris in her old age did it to fourteen Persian boys of distinguished family, by way of a present which she hoped the supposed god of the under-world would accept instead of herself.

From the Strymon the army came to a strip of coast running westward, on which stands the Greek town of Argilus. . . . Thence, keeping the Gulf of Posidium on his left, Xerxes marched through the plain . . . until he arrived at Acanthus. Like the others whom I mentioned before, the inhabitants of these places . . . were pressed into his service, those on the coast being forced to sail with the fleet, those inland to march with the army. The road which the Great King took remains untouched to this day; the Thracians hold it in profound reverence and never plough it up or sow crops on it. . . .

[Now] the Greeks who had to entertain the Persian army and provide a dinner for the king . . . were utterly ruined, and were obliged to leave house and home. For instance, when the Thasians, on behalf of their towns on the mainland, billeted and fed the army, Antipater, the son of Orgeus, a citizen of the highest repute, to whom the arrangements had been entrusted, proved that the meal cost 400 talents of silver. And similar accounts were returned by the officers in the other towns. A great deal of fuss had been made about the meal, and orders for its preparation had been issued a long time in advance; accordingly, the moment that word came from the officers who carried the king's commands, people in every town distributed their stores of grain and employed themselves for months on end in making barley and wheat flour, in buying up and fattening the best cattle they could find, and feeding poultry in coops and waterfowl in ponds, to be ready for the army when it came. In addition to this they ordered the manufacture of drinking cups and mixing-bowls of gold and silver, and of everything else that is needed to adorn the table. All this, of course, was for the king himself and those who dined with him; for the troops in general the preparations were confined to food. On the arrival of the army, there was always a tent ready for Xerxes to take his rest in, while the men bivouacked in the open; but it was when dinner-time came that the real trouble for the unfortunate hosts began. The guests ate their fill and, after spending the night in the place, pulled up the tent next morning, seized the cups and table-gear and everything else it contained, and marched off without leaving a single thing behind. A man of Abdera called Megacreon spoke to the point on this subject, when he advised all the people of the town to take their wives to the temples and pray heaven to continue to spare them one half of their troubles, with proper gratitude for the blessing already received, that King Xerxes was not in the habit of taking *two* dinners a day. It was clear enough that if the orders had been to prepare a morning meal as well as an evening one, the people of Abdera would have had to clear out altogether before Xerxes arrived, or else be hopelessly crushed by the burden of the expense. Nevertheless the various places along the route did manage to carry out their orders, though not without severe suffering.

At Acanthus Xerxes sent the fleet on separately, and ordered the commanders to wait for him at Therma—the town on the gulf to which it has given its name. It was through Therma that he had ascertained his shortest route to lie. From Doriscus to Acanthus the army had been marching in three divisions, of which one under Mardonius and Masistes took the coast road and kept in close touch with the fleet, another under Tritantaechmes and Gergis a parallel route some distance inland, and the third under Smerdomenes and Megabyzus a route between the two. This third division Xerxes himself accompanied. . . .

While the fleet waited near Therma and the Axius and the intervening towns, Xerxes with the army was on his way from Acanthus by the inland road to the rendezvous. He passed through Paeonia and Crestonia to the river Echeidorus, which rises in the latter country and flows through Mygdonia, to reach the sea by way of the marshland at the mouth of the Axius. It was during this march that his pack-camels were attacked by lions, which came down from their haunts at night and never molested either the men or any of the other animals, but only the camels. I am puzzled at what it could have been that made the lions ignore every other living creature and set only upon the camels—beasts which they had never seen, or had any experience of, before. . . .

At Therma Xerxes halted his army, and the troops went into camp. They occupied the whole seaboard from Therma in Myg-

donia to the Lydias and Haliacmon—two rivers which unite
and form the boundary between Bottiaeis and Macedonia. While
they were encamped here, all the rivers I have mentioned supplied enough water for their needs except the Echeidorus, which
failed.

Xerxes could see from Therma the Thessalian mountains—
the towering peaks of Olympus and Ossa—and on being informed that between the two mountains there was a narrow
gorge through which the river Peneus ran, and also a road leading
into Thessaly, he suddenly felt that he would like to go by sea
and inspect the mouth of the river. His intention was to take
the army by the upper road through the inland parts of Macedonia into Perrhaebia, past the town of Gonnus; for that, he
heard, was the safest route. No sooner, therefore, had the fancy
taken him than he acted upon it; and going aboard the Sidonian
vessel which he always used for any such occasion, he gave the
signal to the rest of the fleet to put to sea, leaving the army
behind in its encampments. The appearance of the river-mouth,
on his arrival there, was a great surprise to him, so that he called
the guides and asked them if it was possible to turn the course
of the river so as to bring it to the sea at some other point.
Now it is said that in the remote past Thessaly was a lake—a
not unreasonable supposition, as the whole country is enclosed
by lofty hills. . . . The natives of Thessaly have a tradition that
the gorge which forms the outlet for the river was made by
Poseidon, and the story is a reasonable one; for if one believes
that it is Poseidon who shakes the earth and that chasms caused
by earthquake are attributable to him, then the mere sight of
this place would be enough to make one say that it is Poseidon's
handiwork. It certainly appeared to me that the cleft in the
mountains had been caused by an earthquake.

So when Xerxes asked if there was any other outlet by which
the Peneus could reach the sea, the guides, who were perfectly
familiar with the facts, replied, "No, my lord; there is no other

outlet but this, because the whole of Thessaly is surrounded with a ring of hills, like a crown." At this Xerxes is said to have remarked: "The Thessalians are sensible men; it was with this very danger in view that they made their submission to me in good time—they realized, amongst other things, that their country is easy to take and very vulnerable. Nothing more would have been needed than to flood the country by damming the gorge, and so forcing the river from its present channel; that would have put all Thessaly except the mountains under water." In saying this he had, of course, the Aleuadae in mind—the Thessalian family who were the first Greeks to submit to the Persian king. Doubtless he thought that they had made the offer of friendship in the name of the people generally.

Then, having seen the place, and having made this comment, Xerxes returned by sea to Therma.

His stay in Pieria lasted a number of days, during which one third of his army was felling the forest through the mountains of Macedonia, making a route for his troops to follow into Perrhaebia. Meanwhile the representatives who had been sent to Greece to demand submission rejoined the army—some empty-handed, others bringing the earth and water. Those who gave the tokens of submission were the following: the Thessalians, Dolopes, Aenianes, Perrhaebi, Locrians, Magnetes, Malians, Achaeans of Phthiotis, Thebans, and all the other Boeotians except the people of Plataea and Thespiae. Against these the Greeks who determined to resist the invader swore an oath to the effect that, once the war was fought to a successful conclusion, they would punish all men of Greek blood, who without compulsion yielded to the Persians, and dedicate a tenth part of their property to the God at Delphi.

To Athens and Sparta Xerxes sent no demand for submission because of what happened to the messengers whom Darius had sent on a previous occasion: at Athens they were thrown into the pit like criminals, at Sparta they were pushed into a well

—and told that if they wanted earth and water for the king, to get them from there. This time, therefore, Xerxes refrained from sending a request. Just what disagreeable consequences were suffered by the Athenians for this treatment of the king's messengers, I am unable to say; perhaps it was the destruction of their city and the countryside around it—though I do not myself believe that this happened as a direct result of their crime. The case is clear, however, with respect to the Spartans: upon them fell the anger of Agamemnon's herald Talthybius. There is in Sparta a temple dedicated to Talthybius, and a family—the Talthybiadae—descended from him, which enjoys the sole privilege of holding the office of herald. Now there was a long period after the incident I have mentioned above, during which the Spartans were unable to obtain favourable signs from their sacrifices; this caused them deep concern, and they held frequent assemblies at which the question "Is there any Spartan who is willing to die for his country?" was put by the public crier. Thereupon two Spartans, Sperchias, the son of Aneristus, and Bulis, the son of Nicolas, both men of good family and great wealth, volunteered to offer their lives to Xerxes in atonement for Darius' messengers who had been killed in Sparta. They were dispatched accordingly to Persia to meet their doom. The courage of these two men is indeed admirable, and what followed is no less so. On their way to Susa they visited Hydarnes, a Persian by birth who was in command of the whole Asiatic seaboard; and by him they were given a hospitable welcome and invited to dinner. During the meal Hydarnes said: "Why is it, gentlemen, that you refuse to be friends with the king? You have only to look at me and the position I enjoy to see that he knows how to reward merit. Now Xerxes believes that you, too, are men of merit; and both of you, if only you would submit, might find yourselves in authority over lands in Greece which he would give you."

"Hydarnes," came the answer, "the advice you give us does not spring from a full knowledge of the situation. You know one half of what is involved, but not the other half. You understand well enough what slavery is, but freedom you have never experienced, so you do not know if it tastes sweet or bitter. If you ever did come to experience it, you would advise us to fight for it not with spears only, but with axes too."

After this they continued their journey to Susa, and the first thing that happened when they entered the presence of the king was that the men of the royal bodyguard ordered—and, indeed, attempted to compel—them to fall flat on the ground in the act of worship. The two Spartans, however, declared that they would never do such a thing, even though the guards should push their heads down on to the floor. It was not, they said, the custom in Sparta to worship a mere man like themselves, and it was not for that purpose that they had come to Persia. So they persisted in their refusal, adding words to the following effect: "My lord King of the Medes, the Spartans sent us here to suffer punishment in reparation for the murder of the Persian messengers in Sparta"; to which Xerxes with truly noble generosity replied that he would not behave like the Spartans, who by murdering the ambassadors of a foreign power had broken the law which all the world holds sacred. He had no intention of doing the very thing for which he blamed them, or, by taking reprisals, of freeing the Spartans from the burden of their crime. This conduct on the part of the Spartans succeeded for a time in allaying the anger of Talthybius, in spite of the fact that Sperchias and Bulis returned home alive. . . .

The purpose of Xerxes' expedition, which was directed nominally against Athens, was in fact the conquest of the whole of Greece. The various Greek communities had long been aware of this, but they viewed the coming danger with very different eyes. Some had already made their submission, and were consequently in good spirits, because they were sure of getting off lightly at the invaders' hands; others, who had refused to submit, were thrown into panic partly because there were not enough ships in Greece to meet the Persians with any chance of success, and partly because most of the Greeks were unwilling to fight and all too ready to accept Persian dominion. At this point I find myself compelled to express an opinion which I know most people will object to; nevertheless, as I believe it to be true, I will not suppress it. If the Athenians, through fear of the approaching danger, had abandoned their country, or if they had stayed there and submitted to Xerxes, there would have been no attempt to resist the Persians by sea; and, in the absence of a Greek fleet, it is easy to see what would have been the course of events on land. However many lines of fortification the Spartans had built across the Isthmus, they would have been deserted by their confederates; not that their allies would have wished to desert them, but they could not have helped doing so, because one by one they would have fallen victims to the Persian naval power. Thus the Spartans would have been left alone—to perform prodigies of valour and to die nobly. Or, on the other hand, it is possible that before things came to the ultimate test, the sight of the rest of Greece submitting to Persia might have driven them to make terms with Xerxes. In either case the Persian conquest of Greece would have been assured; for I cannot myself see what possible use there could have been in fortifying the Isthmus, if the Persians had command of the sea. In view of this, therefore, one is surely right in saying that Greece was saved by the Athenians. It was the Athenians who held the balance: whichever side they joined was sure to prevail. It was the Athenians, too, who, having chosen that Greece should live and preserve her freedom, roused to battle the other Greek states which had not yet submitted. It was the Athenians who—after God—drove back the Persian king. Not even the terrifying warnings of the oracle at Delphi could persuade them to abandon Greece; they stood firm and had the courage to meet the invader.

The Athenians had sent their envoys to Delphi really to ask an oracle, and as soon as the customary rites were performed

and they had entered the shrine and taken their seats, the Priestess Aristonice uttered the following prophecy:

> Why sit you, doomed ones? Fly to the world's end, leaving
> Home and the heights your city circles like a wheel.
> The head shall not remain in its place, nor the body,
> Nor the feet beneath, nor the hands, nor the parts between;
> But all is ruined, for fire and the headlong God of War
> Speeding in a Syrian chariot shall bring you low.
> Many a tower shall he destroy, not yours alone,
> And give to pitiless fire many shrines of gods,
> Which even now stand sweating, with fear quivering,
> While over the roof-tops black blood runs streaming
> In prophecy of woe that needs must come. But rise,
> Haste from the sanctuary and bow your hearts to grief.

The Athenian envoys heard these words with dismay; indeed
they were about to abandon themselves to despair at the dreadful
fate which was prophesied, when Timon, the son of Androbulus
and one of the most distinguished men in Delphi, suggested
that they should take branches of olive in their hands and, in
the guise of suppliants, approach the oracle a second time. The
Athenians acted upon this suggestion. "Lord Apollo," they said,
"can you not, in consideration of these olive boughs which we
have brought you, give us some better prophecy about our
country? Otherwise we will never leave the holy place but stay
here till we die."

Thereupon the Prophetess uttered a second prophecy, which
ran as follows:

> Not wholly can Pallas win the heart of Olympian Zeus,
> Though she prays him with many prayers and all her subtlety;
> Yet will I speak to you this other word, as firm as adamant:
> Though all else shall be taken within the bound of Cecrops
> And the fastness of the holy mountain of Cithaeron,
> Yet Zeus the all-seeing grants to Athene's prayer
> That the wooden wall only shall not fall, but help you and
>   your children.

But await not the host of horse and foot coming from Asia,
Nor be still, but turn your back and withdraw from the foe.
Truly a day will come when you will meet him face to face.
Divine Salamis, you will bring death to women's sons
When the corn is scattered, or the harvest gathered in.

This second answer seemed to be, as indeed it was, less menacing than the first; so the envoys wrote it down and returned to Athens. When it was made public upon their arrival in the city, and the attempt to explain it began, amongst the various opinions which were expressed there were two mutually exclusive interpretations. Some of the older men supposed that the prophecy meant that the Acropolis would escape destruction, on the grounds that the Acropolis was fenced in the old days with a thorn-hedge, and that this was the "wooden wall" of the oracle; but others thought that by this expression the oracle meant the ships, and they urged in consequence that everything should be abandoned in favour of the immediate preparation of a fleet. There was, however, for those who believed "wooden wall" to mean ships, one disturbing thing—namely, the last two lines of the Priestess' prophecy:

Divine Salamis, you will bring death to women's sons
When the corn is scattered, or the harvest gathered in.

This was a very awkward statement and caused profound disturbance amongst all who took the wooden wall to signify ships; for the professional interpreters understood the lines to mean that they would be beaten at Salamis in a fight at sea. There was, however, a man in Athens who had recently made a name for himself—Themistocles called Neocles' son; he now came forward and declared that there was an important point in which the professional interpreters were mistaken. If, he maintained, the disaster referred to was to strike the Athenians, it would not have been expressed in such mild language. "Hateful Salamis" would surely have been a more likely phrase than "divine

Salamis," if the inhabitants of the country were doomed to destruction there. On the contrary, the true interpretation was that the oracle referred not to the Athenians but to their enemies. The "wooden wall" did, indeed, mean the ships; so he advised his countrymen to prepare at once to meet the invader at sea.

The Athenians found Themistocles' explanation of the oracle preferable to that of the professional interpreters, who had not only tried to dissuade them from preparing to fight at sea but had been against offering opposition of any sort. The only thing to do was, according to them, to abandon Attica altogether and seek a home elsewhere.

Once on a previous occasion Themistocles had succeeded in getting his views accepted, to the great benefit of his country. The Athenians had amassed a large sum of money from the produce of the mines at Laurium, which they proposed to share out amongst themselves at the rate of ten drachmas a man; Themistocles, however, persuaded them to give up this idea and, instead of distributing the money, to spend it on the construction of two hundred warships for use in the war with Aegina. The outbreak of this war at that moment saved Greece by forcing Athens to become a maritime power. In point of fact the two hundred ships were not employed for the purpose for which they were built, but were available for Greece in her hour of need. The Athenians also found it necessary to expand this existing fleet by laying down new ships, and they determined in debate after the discussion on the oracle to take the god's advice and meet the invader at sea with all the force they possessed, and with any other Greeks who were willing to join them.

At a conference of the Greek states who were loyal to the general cause, guarantees were exchanged, and the decision was reached that the first thing to be done was to patch up their own quarrels and stop any fighting which happened to be going on amongst members of the confederacy. There were a number of such disputes at the time, the most serious being the quarrel between Athens and Aegina. Having learnt that Xerxes and his army had reached Sardis, they next resolved to send spies into Asia to get information about the Persian forces; at the same time, in the hope of uniting, if it were possible, the whole Greek world and of bringing all the various communities to undertake joint action in face of the common danger, they decided to send an embassy to Argos to conclude an alliance, another to Gelon, the son of Dinomenes, in Sicily, and others, again, to Corcyra and Crete. Gelon was said to be very powerful—far more powerful than anyone else of Greek nationality.

These decisions were put into force at once. The private quarrels were made up, and three men sent off to Asia to collect information. They arrived in Sardis and found out all they could about the king's army, but were caught in the process, tortured by the Persian army commanders, and condemned to death. But when Xerxes was told that they were about to be executed, he disapproved of his generals' decision and sent men from his bodyguard with orders, if the three spies were still alive, to bring them before him. As the sentence had not yet been carried out, the spies were brought to the king, who, having satisfied himself about the reason for their presence in Sardis, instructed his guards to take them round and let them see the whole army, infantry and cavalry, and then, when they were satisfied that they had seen everything, to let them go without molestation to whatever country they pleased. After giving this order he explained the purpose of it by pointing out that, if the spies had been executed, the Greeks would not have been able to learn in good time how incalculably great the Persian strength was—and the killing of three men would not have done the enemy much harm; but if, on the other hand, the spies returned home, he was confident that their report on the magnitude of the Persian power would induce the Greeks to surrender their liberty before the actual invasion took place, so that there would be no need to go to the trouble of fighting a war at all. . . .

The Greeks who had united for resistance to Persia next dispatched their representatives to Argos. The Argives themselves explain their subsequent behaviour as follows: they were aware from the beginning of the Persian preparations against Greece, and knew very well that the Greeks would try to enlist their support in meeting the invasion; so they sent to Delphi for advice upon what action would, under the circumstances, be best for them to take. The reason for this step was the fact that six thousand of their men had recently been killed by the Spartans under Cleomenes, the son of Anaxandrides. The Priestess' answer to their question was this:

> Loathed by your neighbours, dear to the immortal gods,
> Hold your javelin within and sit upon your guard.
> Guard the head well, and the head will save the body.

This oracle had already been delivered, when the envoys arrived in Argos, and entered the council-chamber to deliver their message. The Argive answer was, that they were willing to do what they were asked upon two conditions: first, they must obtain a thirty years' truce with Sparta, and, secondly, share with Sparta, on equal terms, the command of the confederate forces. By right Argos was entitled to the sole command; nevertheless they would be content with an equal division.

Such, according to them, was their government's answer, in spite of the fact that the oracle had forbidden them to join the confederacy. Moreover, though they shrank from disobeying the oracle, it was important to them to secure the thirty years' truce, to give their sons the chance of growing up during the period of peace; and if they failed to secure it, and were unlucky enough to suffer another defeat—this time at the hands of the Persians—it seemed only too likely that they would find themselves permanently subject to Sparta. The Spartan envoys replied to the demands of the Argive government by saying that they would refer the question of the truce to their own government at home; on the other matter, however, namely the army command, they already had their instructions, and their answer was that Sparta had two kings and Argos only one, and it was not possible to deprive either of the Spartan kings of his command; on the other hand, there was nothing to prevent the Argive ruler from expressing his views in conjunction with the two Spartans.

The Argives add that they found the Spartan attitude intolerably presumptuous, and, rather than give way to it, they preferred to submit to foreign domination; accordingly they gave notice to the envoys that they must be out of the country before sunset, or be treated as enemies.

So much for the Argive account of this transaction; there is, however, another story current in Greece, to the effect that Xerxes sent a man to Argos before his army started on its march. "Men of Argos," this person is supposed to have said upon his arrival, "King Xerxes has a message for you. We Persians believe that we are descended from Perses, whose father was Danae's son Perseus, and whose mother was Andromeda the daughter of Cepheus. Thus we are of the same blood as yourselves, and it would not be right for us to make war upon the people from whom we have sprung, any more than it would be right for you to help others by opposing us. Rather you should hold aloof from the coming struggle and take no part in it. If things turn out as I hope they will, there is no people I shall hold in greater esteem than you."

The story goes on to say that the Argives were much impressed by Xerxes' message; they made no promises for the moment, and put forward no demand for a share in the command of the army; later, however, when the Greeks were trying to obtain their support, they did make the claim, because they knew that the Spartans would refuse to grant it, and that they would thus have an excuse for taking no part in the war. There are people in Greece who say that this account is borne out by a remark made long afterwards by Artaxerxes. Callias, the son of Hipponicus, and a number of other Athenians were in Susa, the city of Memnon, on quite different business, and it so happened that their visit coincided with that of some representatives from Argos, who had been sent to ask Xerxes' son Artaxerxes if the friendly relations, which the Argives had established with his father, still held good, or if they were now considered by Persia as enemies. "They do indeed hold good," Artaxerxes is said to have replied; "there is no city which I believe to be a better friend to me than Argos."

For my own part I cannot positively state that Xerxes either did, or did not, send the messenger to Argos; nor can I guarantee the story of the Argives going to Susa and asking Artaxerxes about their relationship with Persia. I express no opinion on this matter other than that of the Argives themselves. One thing, however, I am very sure of: and that is, that if all mankind agreed to meet, and everyone brought his own faults along with him for the purpose of exchanging them for somebody else's, there is not a man who, after taking a good look at his neighbour's faults, would not be only too happy to return home with his own. My business is to record what people say, but I am by no means bound to believe it—and that may be taken to apply to this book as a whole. There is yet another story about the Argives: it was they, according to some, who invited the Persians to invade Greece, because their war with Sparta was going badly and they felt that anything would be better than their present sufferings.

Another embassy was sent by the confederates to Sicily, to confer with Gelon. One of the allied representatives was the Spartan Syagrus. . . .

[Herodotus digresses here to tell the story of the Greek despot Gelon's ruthless rise to power and of the flowering of Syracuse under his rule.]

And now the envoys from Greece arrived in Syracuse, approached Gelon, and spoke to the following effect: "We have been sent by the Spartans and their allies to obtain your help against the foreigner. You are, of course, aware of what is coming to Greece; that a Persian is about to bridge the Hellespont and to march against us out of Asia with all the armies of the east at his back, and that his true purpose, which he veils under the pretence of an attack on Athens, is the subjugation of the whole of Greece. Your power is great; as lord of Sicily you possess no inconsiderable portion of the Greek world; we ask you, therefore, to help us, and to add your strength to ours in our struggle to maintain our country's liberty. Greece united will be strong and a match for the invader; but if some of us betray and others stand aside, and only a minority is sound, then there is reason to fear that all Greece may fall. Do not imagine that if the Persians defeat us in battle they will not afterwards visit *you*. They will—so be on your guard in time. By supporting us you will be defending yourself. It usually happens that well-laid plans have a prosperous issue."

Gelon's answer to this speech was made with passionate vehemence. "What," he cried, "have you the face to come here and urge me with your selfish arguments to help you resist a foreign invader? Have you forgotten that I, too, was once at war with a foreign power—the Carthaginians—and that I applied to you for help? Yes, and I begged you to avenge upon the men of Egesta their murder of Dorieus the son of Anaxandrides, and offered to help free the ports which have been the source of such profit and advantage to you. But what was your answer? You refused to come either to help me or to avenge Dorieus' death—and for all you cared, this whole country might now be subject to foreign rule. Well—luck, as it happens, has come my way; the wheel has come full circle and now it is you who are in danger—so you remember Gelon! Nevertheless, though you treated me with contempt, I will not imitate your conduct. I am willing to help you by a contribution of 200 ships of war, 20,000 heavy-armed infantry, 2000 cavalry, 2000 archers, 2000 slingers, and 2000 light horsemen; and I undertake to provision the entire Greek army for as long as the war may last. My offer, however, is subject to one condition—that the supreme command of the Greek forces against the Persians shall be mine. On any other terms I will neither come myself nor send troops."

This was too much for Syagrus, and he burst out: "Agamemnon, son of Pelops, would groan in his grave if he heard that Sparta had been robbed of her command by Gelon and his Syracusans! Let us hear no more of our giving you command. If you wish to help Greece, you must understand that it will be under Spartan leadership. If you dislike the idea of a subordinate position, then you need not help."

Gelon, seeing from what Syagrus said that he was unlikely to accept his terms, made his last proposal. "My Spartan friend," he said, "reproaches have a way of making a man angry; nevertheless in spite of your insults I will answer you with courtesy. Surely, if you maintain so eagerly your right to the command, it is only reasonable that I should urge my own claim more strongly still, as I have a much bigger fleet and an army many times the size of yours. However, since my proposal is so painful to you, I will make some concession: suppose you command the army, and I the navy. Or, if you prefer to command at sea, I am willing to take over the land forces. You must either be content with this, or do without the powerful support I am able to give you."

The Athenian envoy gave Syagrus no time to reply to this, but as soon as Gelon had made his offer, "King of Syracuse," he cried, "Greece did not send us to ask for a commander but for an army. But clearly you are unwilling to send troops unless you have command—the one thing you are set upon getting. Now when you asked for the supreme command of all the Greek forces, we were content to hold our tongues, because we knew that our colleague from Sparta would be quite capable of answering for us both; but things are different now that, having failed in your original claim, you ask to command at sea. Even if Sparta allowed this, we should not. Command of the fleet, provided Sparta herself does not want it, belongs to us. We do not object to Sparta having it if she wishes, but we refuse to give it up to anybody else. What would be the use of our having built up the finest navy in Greece if we surrendered the command of it to the Syracusans? Are we not Athenians—the most ancient of all Greek peoples, the only nation never to have left the soil from which it sprang? Did not the poet Homer say that we sent to Troy the best man for ordering and marshalling an army? Surely, then, we need not be ashamed of speaking as we do."

"My friend," Gelon replied, "it looks as if you have the commanders—but will not have any men for them to command. Since, therefore, you claim everything and yield nothing, you had better go home as quickly as you can and tell Greece that the spring of the year, the fairest of the four seasons, is lost to her."

That was the end of the Greek negotiations with Gelon, and the envoys set out for home.

Gelon himself was afraid that Greece would be unable to survive the Persian invasion; at the same time, as lord of Sicily, he could not bring himself to go to the Peloponnese and submit to taking orders from Spartans. Accordingly he chose a different course. As soon as news came that Xerxes was over the Hellespont, he sent three galleys under the charge of Cadmus, the son of Scythes, a native of Cos, with instructions to go to Delphi, where, equipped with a large sum of money and plenty of friendly words, he was to wait and see how the war would go; then, if the Persians won, he was to give the money to Xerxes together with earth and water of Gelon's dominions. If the Greeks won, he was to bring the money back again.

Some time before this, Cadmus had inherited the position of absolute master of Cos from his father, who had established his power there on firm foundations; yet of his own free will, without threat of violence from any quarter, he had, simply from his sense of justice, abdicated his power and handed it over to the people. He then left home for Sicily, where he took the town of Zancle with the Samians—or Messene, as it was afterwards called—and lived there. This was how Cadmus came to Sicily, and was the reason why Gelon, having had evidence already of his sense of honour, chose him for the mission to Delphi. And now yet another honest action, perhaps the most remarkable of all, was to be added to the former ones: having in his hands the large sum of money which Gelon had entrusted to him, with every opportunity of keeping it, he preferred not to; and after the Greek victory, and the departure of Xerxes, he returned to Sicily with the money intact.

There is a story in Sicily that Gelon would have sent help to Greece in spite of the necessity of serving under Spartan commanders had it not been for the action of Terillus, . . . ruler of Himera. Driven from his home by . . . Theron, the master of Agrigentum, he brought into Sicily just about this time an army 300,000 strong, from Carthage, Libya, Iberia, Liguria, Helisycia, Sardinia, and Corsica—under the command of Hamilcar, . . . king of Carthage. . . . The Sicilians also maintain that the victory of Gelon and Theron over Hamilcar of Carthage took place on the same day as the Greek victory over Persia at Salamis. . . .

The envoys who went to Sicily called also at Corcyra and put their request for help in the same words as they used to Gelon. The immediate result was a promise from the Corcyraeans to send a fleet in support of the alliance. It was impossible, they said, to stand aside and see Greece overwhelmed; they must help her to the utmost of their power, because if she fell not a day would pass before they themselves were reduced to slavery. This answer sounded promising enough, but when the time came to act upon it, the Corcyraeans changed their minds; and having put into commission a fleet of sixty warships, they dawdled about before getting to sea, and then sailed only as far as the Peloponnese, where they hung round in the neighbourhood of Pylos and Taenarum, waiting, like Gelon, to see the result of the fighting. They thought it most unlikely that the Greeks would win; the Persians, in their opinion, would gain a complete victory and make themselves masters of all Greece. Their conduct was deliberately designed to enable them to say, in this event, to Xerxes that, though they might have answered the Greek appeal for aid by sending a fleet second in strength only to that of Athens, they had refused to do so, not wishing to oppose him or to take any action which he would not like. They hoped, no doubt, that this would get them better treatment than the other Greek states—and so, indeed, it would have done, I admit. They also had an excuse ready to offer to the Greeks—and used it when the time came and they were reproached for their failure to send assistance. The excuse was that they had fitted out sixty ships, but had been prevented by prevailing north-easters from getting round Cape Malea: this explained their absence from the battle of Salamis—an absence in no way due to disloyalty or cowardice.

The Cretans, on the arrival of the Greek envoys with their appeal, sent to Delphi to inquire jointly whether or not it would be to their advantage to make common cause with Greece. "Foolish men," the oracle replied, "do you not still resent all the tears which Minos in his anger caused you to weep after you helped Menelaus? Was he not angry because they did not help you to avenge his death at Camicus, whereas you did help them to avenge the rape by a foreign prince of a woman from Sparta?" When the Cretans heard that answer, they refrained from joining the alliance. . . .

According to the tradition in Praesus, men of various nationality, but especially Greeks, came to settle in Crete after it was depopulated by the expedition to Sicily; then in the third generation after the death of Minos came the Trojan war, in which the Cretans proved themselves by no means the most despicable champions of Menelaus; their reward for this service on their return home was famine and plague for both men and cattle, so that for the second time Crete was denuded of its population. Thus it happens that the present Cretans, together with the remnant of the former population, are the third people to live in the island. It was these events of which the Delphic Priestess reminded the Cretans in her answer to their question, and thereby prevented them from joining the Greek confederacy in spite of their readiness to do so.

The Thessalians did not submit to Persia until they were compelled, for they showed plainly enough that the intrigues of the Aleuadae were not to their liking. No sooner had the news reached them of the imminent crossing of the Persian army into Europe than they sent representatives to the Isthmus, where delegates from all Greek towns loyal to the common cause were assembled. On their arrival the Thessalian delegates addressed the assembly in these terms: "Fellow countrymen, in order to save Thessaly and the whole of Greece, it is necessary to defend the passage past Mt. Olympus. We are ready to assist you in the defence of this vital pass, and you, for your part, must send a strong force. If you fail to do so, we give you fair warning that we shall come to terms with Persia. We are in an exposed position, and cannot be expected, alone and unassisted, to give our lives merely to save the rest of you. If you are unwilling to send us aid, you cannot compel us to fight your battle for you; for sheer inability is stronger than any compulsion. We shall try to devise some means of saving ourselves."

The Greek answer was to determine to send an army by sea to Thessaly, to defend the pass. The troops assembled and, after passing through the Euripus, came to Alus in Achaea, where they left the ships and proceeded to Thessaly on foot. Here they occupied Tempe, the pass which leads from lower Macedonia into Thessaly along the Peneus, between Mt. Olympus and Mt. Ossa. It was here that some 10,000 Greek heavy infantry, reinforced by the Thessalian cavalry, took up their position. The Spartans were commanded by Euanetus son of Carenus, who had been chosen for the post from the Polemarchs, though he was not of the royal blood; the Athenians were commanded by Themistocles, son of Neocles. But the army had not been in Tempe many days when a message arrived from Alexander, the son of Amyntas, in Macedonia advising the Greek troops to withdraw, and not stay in the pass to be trampled underfoot, adding an indication of the strength of the Persian army and fleet. The advice seemed to be sound, and was clearly offered by the Macedonian in a friendly spirit, so the Greeks took it. I think myself that what persuaded them to go was the alarm they felt upon learning that there was another way into Thessaly through upper Macedonia and Perrhaebia, near Gonnus—the pass, in fact, by which Xerxes' army actually did come in.

The Greeks, then, re-embarked and returned to the Isthmus. Such were the circumstances of the expedition to Thessaly—it took place while Xerxes was at Abydos, just before he crossed the strait from Asia into Europe. The result of it was that the Thessalians, finding themselves without support, no longer hesitated but whole-heartedly worked in the Persian interest, so that in the course of the war they proved of the greatest use to Xerxes.

The Greeks on their return to the Isthmus then discussed, in consideration of the warning they had received from Alexander, where they should make a stand. The proposal which found most favour was to guard the pass of Thermopylae, on the grounds that it was narrower than the pass into Thessaly and at the same time nearer home. They knew nothing as yet about the mountain track by means of which the men who fell at Thermopylae were taken in the rear, and only learnt of its existence from the people of Trachis after their arrival.

The decision, then, was to hold the pass in order to prevent the Persians from entering Greece, and at the same time to send the fleet to Artemisium on the coast of Histiaea; for these two places being close together, communication would be easy. The topography is as follows: Artemisium is where the sea south of Thrace contracts into a narrow channel between the island of Sciathos and the mainland of Magnesia; pass through this channel and you come to the strip of coast called Artemisium. It is a part of Euboea, and contains a temple of Artemis. The pass through Trachis into Greece is, at Thermopylae, fifty feet wide; elsewhere, both east and west of Thermopylae, it is still narrower; at Alpeni to the eastward, it is only a single waggon track, and to the westward near Anthela on the river Phoenix it is about the same. To the southwest—inland—there is no way through, passage being barred by a lofty and precipitous ascent, running up to Mt. Oeta, while on the other side of the roadway is the sea, full of banks and shoals. There are hot springs in the pass—known locally as the Basins—with an altar over them dedicated to Heracles. A wall was once built across this passage, and there used long ago to be a gateway in it; both were constructed by the Phocians in fear of an invasion from Thessaly, at the period when the Thessalians came from Thesprotia to settle in the country of Aeolis, which they still occupy. The new settlers tried to overrun Phocis, and the Phocians raised the wall as a protective measure, and at the same time turned the water from the hot springs over the pass, to cut up the ground into gullies, resorting to every device to keep the Thessalians out. The wall had been built a very long time ago and most of it had fallen into ruin through age; now, however, it was decided to rebuild it, and to use it to help stop the Persians from getting through into Greece. Quite close to the road is a village called Alpeni, from which the Greeks counted upon drawing supplies.

These, then, were the places which the Greeks thought would best suit their purpose; careful consideration of all the circumstances, and the realization that the Persians would be unable, in the narrow pass, to use their cavalry or take advantage of their numbers, determined them to make their stand at this point against the invader; so when news came that the enemy was in Pieria, they broke up from the Isthmus and proceeded to their new positions, some on foot to Thermopylae, others by sea to Artemisium.

Meanwhile, as the Greek troops hurried to their stations, the people of Delphi, in great alarm for their own safety and for Greece, applied to their oracle for advice. "Pray to the winds," was the answer; "for they will be good allies to Greece." The first thing the Delphians did upon receiving this oracular counsel was to report it to the Greek states who were determined to fight for their freedom; and, by thus communicating the divine message at a time when Greece was in the grip of fear at the prospect of invasion, they earned everlasting gratitude. Subsequently they consecrated an altar to the winds at Thyia—a place named after Cephisus' daughter, who has a shrine there—and offered sacrifice upon it to the winds in supplication. In memory of this oracle the Delphians still, to this day, pray to the winds for favour.

Xerxes' fleet now left Therma, and ten of the fastest ships set a course direct for Sciathos, where three Greek vessels, one from Troezen, one from Aegina, and one from Attica, were on the look-out. At the first glimpse of the enemy all three fled. The Persians gave chase; the ship from Troezen, under the command of Prexinus, fell into their hands at once, and her captors, picking out the best-looking of the fighting men on board, took him up forward and cut his throat, thinking, no doubt, that the sacrifice of their first handsome Greek prisoner would benefit their cause. The unfortunate man's name was Leon—and possibly his name had something to do with his fate. The trireme from Aegina, commanded by Asonides, gave the Persians some trouble. One of the soldiers on board—Pytheas, the son of

Ischenous—distinguished himself that day; for after the ship was taken, he continued to resist until he was nearly cut to pieces. At last he fell, but, as there was still breath in his body, the Persian troops, anxious to do all they could to save the life of so brave a man, dressed his wounds with myrrh and bound them up with linen bandages. On returning to their base, they exhibited their prisoner admiringly to everybody there, and treated him with much kindness. The other prisoners from this ship were treated merely as slaves.

Two of the three Greek vessels thus fell into Persian hands; the third, commanded by the Athenian Phormos, went ashore, while trying to escape, at the mouth of the Peneus. Here she was taken, though the men in her got away; for the instant the vessel grounded the Athenians aboard leapt out and made their way back to Athens through Thessaly.

News of what had happened was flashed to the Greeks at Artemisium by fire-signal from Sciathos. In the panic which ensued they left their station and moved to Chalcis, intending to guard the Euripus, and leaving look-outs on the high ground of Euboea. Three of the ten Persian ships ran aground on the Ant, a sunken reef between Sciathos and Magnesia; in consequence of this the Persians marked the reef with a stone beacon, after which, the danger being removed, the whole fleet set sail from Therma, eleven days after Xerxes had marched from the town with his army. The Ant lies right in the fairway; Pammon, a native of Scyros, took the Persians to it when they erected their beacon. A day's voyage brought the Persian fleet to Sepias in Magnesia and the strip of coast between Cape Sepias and the town of Casthanea.

The Persian fleet got as far as Sepias, and the army as far as Thermopylae, without loss. . . .

[Herodotus now calculates the Persian army as consisting, in all, of 5,283,320 men.]

So much for the actual army and its attendants; as for eunuchs, female cooks, and soldiers' women, no one could attempt an estimate of their number, any more than of the various pack-animals and Indian dogs which followed the army. They were far too numerous to count. I am not surprised that with so many people and so many beasts the rivers sometimes failed to provide enough water; what does surprise me is that the food never gave out, for I reckon that if no more than a quart of meal was the daily ration for one man, the total daily consumption would have amounted to 110,340 bushels—and this without counting what was consumed by the women, eunuchs, pack-animals, and dogs. Amongst all these immense numbers there was not a man who, for stature and noble bearing, was more worthy than Xerxes to wield so vast a power.

The Persian fleet, as I have mentioned, made the Magnesian coast between Casthanea and Cape Sepias, and on its arrival the leading ships made fast to the land, while the remainder, as there was not much room on the short stretch of beach, came to anchor and lay off-shore in lines, eight deep. In this position they remained during the night; but at dawn next day the weather, which was clear and calm, suddenly changed, and the fleet was caught in a heavy blow from the east—a "Hellespontian," as the people there call it—which raised a confused sea like a pot on the boil. Those who realized in time that the blow was coming, and all who happened to be lying in a convenient position, managed to beach their vessels and to get them clear of the water before they were damaged, and thus saved their own lives as well; but the ships which were caught offshore were driven some on to the place called the Ovens at the foot of Mt. Pelion, others on to the beach itself; a number were driven on to Sepias, and others, again, were forced ashore off the towns of Meliboea and Casthanea. The storm was very violent and there was no chance of riding it out.

There is a story that the Athenians had called upon Boreas to help them, in consequence of another oracle, by which they were advised to "ask the assistance of their son-in-law." Boreas, according to Greek legend, married a woman of Attica, Erechtheus' daughter Orithyia, and in consequence of this marriage the Athenians (so the tale goes) supposed Boreas to be their son-in-law; so when they observed from their station at Chalcis in Euboea that it was coming on to blow—or possibly even sooner—they offered sacrifice to Boreas and Orithyia and begged them to come to their aid and to repeat the former disaster at Athos by once again destroying the Persian fleet. I cannot say if this was really the reason why the fleet was caught at anchor by the north-easter, but the Athenians are quite positive about it: Boreas, they maintain, had helped them before, and it was Boreas who was responsible for what occurred on this occasion too. On their return home they built him a shrine by the river Ilissus.

Four hundred ships, at the lowest estimate, are said to have been lost in this disaster, and the loss of life and of treasure was beyond reckoning. . . . The number of merchant vessels and other craft lost in the storm was too great to reckon. Indeed, such was the magnitude of the disaster that the Persian naval commanders, fearing that the Thessalians might take advantage of their desperate plight to attack them, protected themselves by building a high barricade out of the wreckage. The storm lasted three days, after which the Magi brought it to an end by sacrificial offerings, and by putting spells on the wind, and by further offerings to Thetis and the sea-nymphs—or, of course, it may be that the wind just dropped naturally. . . .

On the second day of the storm the look-out men on the Euboean hills came hurrying to the Greeks and described in detail the destruction of the Persian ships. On hearing the news, they offered prayers of thanksgiving and libations of wine to Poseidon their saviour, and made all speed to return to their station at Artemisium, in the expectation that only a few ships would be left to oppose them. For the second time, therefore, they lay off Artemisium. From that day to this they have always addressed Poseidon by the title of Saviour.

Meanwhile, after the wind had dropped and the sea had gone down, the Persians got the ships they had hauled ashore into the water again, and proceeded along the coast round the southern point of Magnesia straight into the bay which leads to Pagasae. . . .

Fifteen of the Persian ships were far behind in getting under way, and the men aboard, happening to catch sight of the Greek ships at Artemisium, mistook them for their own, and on making towards them fell into the enemies' hands. . . . The Greeks questioned . . . [their] prisoners on all they wished to know about Xerxes' forces, and then sent them away in chains to the Isthmus of Corinth.

Meanwhile the Persian fleet, with the exception of [these] fifteen ships . . . , arrived safely at Aphetae. Two days previously Xerxes with the army had passed through Thessaly and Achaea and entered the country of the Malians. While he was in Thessaly he had held races between the native horses and his own, because he had heard that the horses of Thessaly were the best in Greece. The Greek mares were, however, soundly beaten. . . .

The position, then, was that Xerxes was lying with his force at Trachis in Malian territory, while the Greeks occupied the pass known locally as Pylae—though Thermopylae is the common Greek name. Such were the respective positions of the two armies, one being in control of all the country from Trachis northward, the other of the whole mainland to the south. The Greek force which here awaited the coming of Xerxes was made up of the following contingents: 300 heavy-armed infantry from Sparta, 500 from Tegea, 500 from Mantinea, 120 from Orchomenus in Arcadia, 1000 from the rest of Arcadia; from Corinth there were 400, from Phlius 200, and from Mycenae 80. In addition to these troops from the Peloponnese, there were the Boeotian contingents of 700 from Thespiae and 400 from

Thebes. The Locrians of Opus and the Phocians had also obeyed the call to arms, the former sending all the men they had, the latter one thousand. The other Greeks had induced these two towns to send troops by a message to the effect that they themselves were merely an advance force, and that the main body of the confederate army was daily expected; the sea, moreover, was strongly held by the fleet of Athens and Aegina and the other naval forces. Thus there was no cause for alarm—for, after all, it was not a god who threatened Greece, but a man, and there neither was nor ever would be a man who was not born with a good chance of misfortune—and the greater the man, the greater the misfortune. The present enemy was no exception; he too was human, and was sure to be disappointed of his great expectations.

The appeal succeeded, and Opus and Phocis sent their troops to Trachis. The contingents of the various states were under their own officers, but the most respected was Leonidas the Spartan, who was in command of the whole army. Leonidas traced his descent directly back to Heracles. . . . He had come to be king of Sparta quite unexpectedly, for as he had two elder brothers, Cleomenes and Dorieus, he had no thought of himself succeeding to the throne. Dorieus, however, was killed in Sicily, and when Cleomenes also died without an heir, Leonidas found himself next in the succession. He was older than Cleombrotus, Anaxandrides' youngest son, and was, moreover, married to Cleomenes' daughter. The three hundred men whom he brought on this occasion to Thermopylae were chosen by himself, all fathers of living sons. He also took with him the Thebans I mentioned, under the command of Leontiades, the son of Eurymachus. The reason why he made a special point of taking troops from Thebes, and from Thebes only, was that the Thebans were strongly suspected of Persian sympathies, so he called upon them to play their part in the war in order to see if they would answer the call, or openly refuse to join the confederacy. They did send troops, but their secret sympathy was nevertheless with the enemy. Leonidas and his three hundred were sent by Sparta in advance of the main army, in order that the sight of them might encourage the other confederates to fight and prevent them from going over to the enemy, as they were quite capable of doing if they knew that Sparta was hanging back; the intention was, when the Carneia was over (for it was that festival which prevented the Spartans from taking the field in the ordinary way), to leave a garrison in the city and march with all the troops at their disposal. The other allied states proposed to act similarly; for the Olympic festival happened to fall just at this same period. None of them ever expected the battle at Thermopylae to be decided so soon—which was the reason why they sent only advance parties there.

The Persian army was now close to the pass, and the Greeks, suddenly doubting their power to resist, held a conference to consider the advisability of retreat. It was proposed by the Peloponnesians generally that the army should fall back upon the Peloponnese and hold the Isthmus; but when the Phocians and Locrians expressed their indignation at this suggestion, Leonidas gave his voice for staying where they were and sending, at the same time, an appeal for reinforcements to the various states of the confederacy, as their numbers were inadequate to cope with the Persians.

During the conference Xerxes sent a man on horseback to ascertain the strength of the Greek force and to observe what the troops were doing. He had heard before he left Thessaly that a small force was concentrated here, led by the Lacedaemonians under Leonidas of the house of Heracles. The Persian rider approached the camp and took a thorough survey of all he could see—which was not, however, the whole Greek army; for the men on the further side of the wall which, after its reconstruction, was now guarded, were out of sight. He did, nonetheless, carefully observe the troops who were stationed on the outside of the wall. At that moment these happened to be the Spartans, and some of them were stripped for exercise, while others were combing their hair. The Persian spy watched them in astonishment; nevertheless he made sure of their numbers, and of everything else he needed to know, as accurately as he could, and then rode quietly off. No one attempted to catch him, or took the least notice of him.

Back in his own camp he told Xerxes what he had seen. Xerxes was bewildered; the truth, namely that the Spartans were preparing themselves to die and deal death with all their strength, was beyond his comprehension, and what they were doing seemed to him merely absurd. Accordingly he sent for Demaratus, the son of Ariston, who had come with the army, and questioned him about the spy's report, in the hope of finding out what the behaviour of the Spartans might mean. "Once before," Demaratus said, "when we began our march against Greece, you heard me speak of these men. I told you then how I saw this enterprise would turn out, and you laughed at me. I strive for nothing, my lord, more earnestly than to observe the truth in your presence; so hear me once more. These men have come to fight us for possession of the pass, and for that struggle they are preparing. It is the common practice of the Spartans to pay careful attention to their hair when they are about to risk their lives. But I assure you that if you can defeat these men and the rest of the Spartans who are still at home, there is no other people in the world who will dare to stand firm or lift a hand against you. You have now to deal with the finest kingdom in Greece, and with the bravest men."

Xerxes, unable to believe what Demaratus said, asked further how it was possible that so small a force could fight with his army. "My lord," Demaratus replied, "treat me as a liar, if what I have foretold does not take place." But still Xerxes was unconvinced.

For four days Xerxes waited, in constant expectation that the Greeks would make good their escape; then, on the fifth, when still they had made no move and their continued presence seemed mere impudent and reckless folly, he was seized with rage and sent forward the Medes and Cissians with orders to take them alive and bring them into his presence. The Medes charged, and in the struggle which ensued many fell; but others took their places, and in spite of terrible losses refused to be beaten off. They made it plain enough to anyone, and not least to the king himself, that he had in his army many men, indeed, but few soldiers. All day the battle continued; the Medes, after their rough handling, were at length withdrawn and their place was taken by Hydarnes and his picked Persian troops—the King's Immortals—who advanced to the attack in full confidence of bringing the business to a quick and easy end. But, once engaged, they were no more successful than the Medes had been; all went as before, the two armies fighting in a confined space, the Persians using shorter spears than the Greeks and having no advantage from their numbers.

On the Spartan side it was a memorable fight; they were men who understood war pitted against an inexperienced enemy, and amongst the feints they employed was to turn their backs on a body and pretend to be retreating in confusion, whereupon the enemy would pursue them with a great clatter and roar; but the Spartans, just as the Persians were on them, would wheel and face them and inflict in the new struggle innumerable casualties. The Spartans had their losses too, but not many. At last the Persians, finding that their assaults upon the pass, whether by divisions or by any other way they could think of, were all useless, broke off the engagement and withdrew. Xerxes was watching the battle from where he sat; and it is said that in the course of the attacks three times, in terror for his army, he leapt to his feet.

Next day the fighting began again, but with no better success for the Persians, who renewed their onslaught in the hope that the Greeks, being so few in number, might be badly enough disabled by wounds to prevent further resistance. But the Greeks never slackened; their troops were ordered in divisions corresponding to the states from which they came, and each division took its turn in the line except the Phocian, which had been posted to guard the track over the mountains. So when the Persians found that things were no better for them than on the previous day, they once more withdrew.

How to deal with the situation Xerxes had no idea; but just then, a man from Malis, Ephialtes, the son of Eurydemus, came, in hope of a rich reward, to tell the king about the track which led over the hills to Thermopylae—and thus he was to prove the death of the Greeks who held the pass.

Later on, Ephialtes, in fear of the Spartans, fled to Thessaly, and in his absence a price was put upon his head by the Amphictyons assembled at Pylae. Some time afterwards he returned to Anticyra, where he was killed by Athenades of Trachis. Athenades killed him not for his treachery but for another reason, which I will explain further on; but the Spartans honoured him nonetheless on that account. According to another story, it was Onetes, the son of Phanagoras of Carystus, and Corydallus of Anticyra who spoke to Xerxes and showed the Persians the way round by the mountain track. This is entirely unconvincing, my first criterion being the fact that the Amphictyons, presumably after careful inquiry, set a price not upon Onetes and Corydallus but upon Ephialtes of Trachis, and my second, that there is no doubt that the accusation of treachery was the reason for Ephialtes' flight. Certainly Onetes, even though he was not a native of Malis, might have known about the track, if he had spent much time in the neighbourhood—but it was Ephialtes, and no one else, who showed the Persians the way, and I leave his name on record as the guilty one.

Xerxes found Ephialtes' offer most satisfactory. He was delighted with it, and promptly sent off Hydarnes with the troops under his command. They left camp about the time the lamps are lit.

The track was originally discovered by the Malians of the neighbourhood; they afterwards used it to help the Thessalians, taking them over it to attack Phocis at the time when the Phocians were protected from invasion by the wall which they had built across the pass. So long, then, have its sinister uses been known to the Malians! . . .

This, then, was the mountain track which the Persians took, after crossing the Asopus. They marched throughout the night, with the mountains of Leta on their right hand and those of Trachis on their left. By early dawn they were at the summit of the ridge, near the spot where the Phocians, as I mentioned before, stood on guard with a thousand men, to watch the track and protect their country. The Phocians had volunteered for this service to Leonidas, the lower road being held as already described.

The ascent of the Persians had been concealed by the oak-woods which cover all these hills, and it was only when they were up that the Phocians became aware of their approach; for there was no wind, and the marching feet made a loud swishing and rustling in the fallen leaves. Leaping to their feet, the Phocians were in the act of arming themselves when the enemy was upon them. The Persians were surprised at the sight of troops preparing to resist; they had expected no opposition—yet here was a body of men barring their way. Hydarnes asked Ephialtes who they were, for his first uncomfortable thought was that they might be Spartans; but on learning the truth he prepared to engage them. The Persian arrows flew thick and fast, and the Phocians, supposing themselves to be the main object of the attack, hurriedly withdrew to the highest point of the mountain, where they made ready to face destruction. But the Persians with Ephialtes and Hydarnes paid no further attention to them, but passed on along the descending track with all possible speed.

The Greeks at Thermopylae had their first warning of the death that was coming with the dawn from the seer Megistias, who read their doom in the victims of sacrifice; deserters, too,

came in during the night with news of the Persian flank movement, and lastly, just as day was breaking, the look-out men
came running from the hills. In council of war their opinions
were divided, some urging that they must not abandon their
post, others the opposite. The result was that the army split:
some dispersed, contingents returning to their various cities,
while others made ready to stand by Leonidas. It is said that
Leonidas himself dismissed them, to spare their lives, but thought
it unbecoming for the Spartans under his command to desert
the post which they had originally come to guard. I myself am
inclined to think that he dismissed them when he realized that
they had no heart for the fight and were unwilling to take their
share of the danger; at the same time honour forbade that he
himself should go. And indeed by remaining at his post he left
a great name behind him, and Sparta did not lose her prosperity,
as might otherwise have happened; for right at the outset of
the war the Spartans had been told by the Delphic oracle that
either their city must be laid waste by the foreigner or a Spartan
king be killed. The prophecy was in hexameter verse and ran
as follows:

> Hear your fate, O dwellers in Sparta of the wide spaces;
> Either your famed, great town must be sacked by Perseus' sons,
> Or, if that be not, the whole land of Lacedaemon
> Shall mourn the death of a king of the house of Heracles,
> For not the strength of lions or of bulls shall hold him,
> Strength against strength; for he has the power of Zeus,
> And will not be checked till one of these two he has consumed.

I believe it was the thought of this oracle, combined with
his wish to lay up for the Spartans a treasure of fame in which
no other city should share, that made Leonidas dismiss those
troops; I do not think that they deserted, or went off without
orders, because of a difference of opinion. Moreover, I am strongly
supported in this view by the case of the seer Megistias, who
was with the army—an Acarnanian, said to be of the clan of

Melampus—who foretold the coming doom from his inspection of the sacrificial victims. He quite plainly received orders from Leonidas to quit Thermopylae, to save them from sharing the army's fate. He refused to go, but he sent his only son, who was serving with the forces.

Thus it was that the confederate troops, by Leonidas' orders, abandoned their posts and left the pass, all except the Thespians and the Thebans who remained with the Spartans. The Thebans were detained by Leonidas as hostages very much against their will; but the Thespians of their own accord refused to desert Leonidas and his men, and stayed, and died with them. They were under the command of Demophilus the son of Diadromes.

In the morning Xerxes poured a libation to the rising sun, and then waited till it was well up before he began to move forward. This was according to Ephialtes' instructions, for the way down from the ridge is much shorter and more direct than the long and circuitous ascent. As the Persian army advanced to the assault, the Greeks under Leonidas, knowing that they were going to their deaths, went out into the wider part of the pass much further than they had done before; in the previous days' fighting they had been holding the wall and making sorties from behind it into the narrow neck, but now they fought outside the narrows. Many of the invaders fell; behind them the company commanders plied their whips indiscriminately, driving the men on. Many fell into the sea and were drowned, and still more were trampled to death by their friends. No one could count the number of the dead. The Greeks, who knew that the enemy were on their way round by the mountain track and that death was inevitable, put forth all their strength and fought with fury and desperation. By this time most of their spears were broken, and they were killing Persians with their swords.

In the course of that fight Leonidas fell, having fought most gallantly, and many distinguished Spartans with him—their names I have learned, as those of men who deserve to be remembered; indeed, I have learned the names of all the three hundred. Amongst the Persian dead, too, were many men of high distinction, including two brothers of Xerxes. . . .

There was a bitter struggle over the body of Leonidas; four times the Greeks drove the enemy off, and at last by their valour rescued it. So it went on, until the troops with Ephialtes were close at hand; and then, when the Greeks knew that they had come, the character of the fighting changed. They withdrew again into the narrow neck of the pass, behind the wall, and took up a position in a single compact body—all except the Thebans—on the little hill at the entrance to the pass, where the stone lion in memory of Leonidas stands to-day. Here they resisted to the last, with their swords, if they had them, and, if not, with their hands and teeth, until the Persians, coming on from the front over the ruins of the wall and closing in from behind, finally overwhelmed them with missile weapons.

Of all the Spartans and Thespians who fought so valiantly the most signal proof of courage was given by the Spartan Dieneces. It is said that before the battle he was told by a native of Trachis that, when the Persians shot their arrows, there were so many of them that they hid the sun. Dieneces, however, quite unmoved by the thought of the strength of the Persian army, merely remarked: "This is pleasant news that the stranger from Trachis brings us: if the Persians hide the sun, we shall have our battle in the shade." He is said to have left on record other sayings, too, of a similar kind, by which he will be remembered. . . .

The dead were buried where they fell, and with them the men who had been killed before those dismissed by Leonidas left the pass. Over them is this inscription, in honour of the whole force:

> Four thousand here from Pelops' land
> Against three million once did stand.

The Spartans have a special epitaph; it runs:

> Go tell the Spartans, you who read:
> We took their orders, and are dead.

For the seer Megistias there is the following:

> Here lies Megistias, who died
> When the Mede passed Spercheius' tide.
> A prophet; yet he scorned to save
> Himself, but shared the Spartans' grave.

The columns with the epitaphs inscribed on them were erected in honour of the dead by the Amphictyons—though the epitaph upon the seer Megistias was the work of Simonides, the son of Leoprepes, who put it there for friendship's sake.

Two of the three hundred Spartans, Eurytus and Aristodemus, are said to have been suffering from acute inflammation of the eyes, on account of which they were dismissed by Leonidas before the battle and went to Alpeni to recuperate. These two men might have agreed together to return in safety to Sparta; or, if they did not wish to do so, they might have shared the fate of their friends. But, unable to agree which course to take, they quarrelled, and Eurytus had no sooner heard that the Persians had made their way round by the mountain track than he called for his armour, put it on, and ordered his servant to lead him to the scene of the battle. The servant obeyed, and then took to his heels, and Eurytus, plunging into the thick of things, was killed. Aristodemus, on the other hand, finding that his heart failed him, stayed behind at Alpeni. Now if only Aristodemus had been involved—if he alone had returned sick to Sparta—or if they had both gone back together, I do not think that the Spartans would have been angry; but as one was killed and the other took advantage of the excuse, which was open to both of them, to save his skin, they could hardly help being very angry indeed with Aristodemus.

There is another explanation of how Aristodemus got back alive to Sparta: according to this, he was sent from camp with a message, and though he might have returned in time to take part in the fighting, he deliberately loitered on the way and so saved himself, while the man who accompanied him on the errand joined in the battle and was killed. In any case, he was met upon his return with reproach and disgrace; no Spartan would give him a light to kindle his fire, or speak to him, and he was nicknamed the Trembler. However, he afterwards made amends for everything at the battle of Plataea.

There is also a story that one more of the three hundred—Pantites—survived. He had been sent with a message into Thessaly, and on his return to Sparta found himself in such disgrace that he hanged himself.

The Thebans under Leontiades remained for a time with the army and were compelled to make some show of resistance to the enemy; but as soon as they saw that things were going in favour of Persia, they took the opportunity of Leonidas' hurried retreat to the little hill, where his last stand was made, to detach themselves from his force; they then approached the enemy with outstretched hands, crying out that in their zeal for the Persian interest they had been amongst the first to give earth and water to the king, and had no share in the responsibility for the injury done him, because they had come to Thermopylae against their will. It was all too true—and, when it was backed up by the evidence of the Thessalians, it saved their lives. Nevertheless, their luck did not hold in every respect; for a few were killed by the Persians on their first approach, and all the rest were branded by Xerxes' orders with the royal mark, beginning with Leontiades their commander. . . .

Such, then, is the story of the Greeks' struggle at Thermopylae. Xerxes, when the battle was over, summoned Demaratus to ask him some questions. "Demaratus," he began, "you are a good man—the truth of your words proves it. Everything has

turned out as you said it would. Now tell me—how many more
Lacedaemonians are there? And how many of them are as good
soldiers as these were? Or are they all as good?" "Sire," Demaratus answered, "there are a great many men and many towns
in Lacedaemon; but what you really want to know I will now
tell you: there is in that country a town called Sparta, which
contains about eight thousand men. All these are the equals of
those who fought in this battle. The other men in Lacedaemon
are not their equals—but good soldiers nonetheless."

"Demaratus," said Xerxes, "tell me what you think would
be the easiest way of defeating these people. You were once
their king, so you must be well acquainted with all the ins and
outs of their policy."

"Sire," replied Demaratus, "if you are really serious in asking
my advice, I am bound to tell you what I consider the best
plan. Suppose you send three hundred ships from the fleet to
Lacedaemon. Off the coast there is an island called Cythera—
Chilon, the wisest man who ever lived amongst us, once said
that it would be better for the Spartans if it were sunk beneath
the sea, for he always expected that it would provide such just
an opportunity for a hostile force as what I am now suggesting.
It was not, of course, your attack that he foresaw—it was the
prospect of any attack from any quarter that alarmed him. This,
then, is my proposal: let your ships make Cythera their base,
and from it spread terror over Lacedaemon. With a war of their
own, on their own doorstep, as it were, you need not fear that
they will help the other Greeks while your army is engaged in
conquering them. Thus the rest of Greece will be crushed first
and Lacedaemon will be left alone and helpless. On the other
hand, if you decide against this plan, you may expect more
trouble; for there is a narrow isthmus in the Peloponnese, and
in it you will find all the troops from that part of Greece who
have formed a league to resist you, and you will have to face
bloodier battles than any you have yet witnessed. But if you

take my advice, the Isthmus and the Peloponnesian towns will fall into your hands without a blow."

Achaemenes, Xerxes' brother and commander of the fleet, who happened to be present and was afraid Xerxes might be persuaded to adopt Demaratus' proposal, spoke in answer: "My lord," he said, "I see that you are allowing yourself to be influenced by a man who envies your success, and is probably a traitor to you. He is a typical Greek, and this is just how they love to behave—envying anyone else's good fortune and hating any power greater than their own. In our present circumstances, when we have already had four hundred ships wrecked, if you detach another three hundred from the fleet for a voyage round the Peloponnese, the enemy will be a match for us. Keep the fleet together, and they will never dare risk an engagement— the disparity in numbers will see to that; moreover, if fleet and army keep in touch and advance together, each can support the other; separate them, and you will be no more use to the fleet than the fleet to you. Only lay your own plans soundly, and you can afford not to worry about the enemy, or to keep wondering what they will do, how many they are, or where they will elect to make a stand. They are quite capable of managing their own affairs, just as we are of managing ours. If the Spartans risk another battle with us, they will certainly not repair the injury they have already received."

"Achaemenes," Xerxes replied, "I think you are right, and I will take your advice. Nevertheless, though Demaratus' judgement is not so good as yours, he told me in good faith what he thought best for me. I will not accept your suggestion that he is secretly hostile to my cause; I have evidence of his loyalty in what he has said on previous occasions, and, apart from that, there is the well-known fact that a man often hates his next-door neighbour and is jealous of his success, and when asked for advice will not tell him what he really thinks will help him most—unless, indeed, he is a man of exceptional virtue, such as one seldom finds. But the relationship between men of different countries is very different from that between men of the same town; a man is full of sympathy for the good fortune of a foreign friend, and will always give him the best advice he can. Demaratus is a foreigner and my guest; I should be obliged, therefore, if everyone would refrain from maligning him in future."

After this conversation Xerxes went over the battlefield to see the bodies, and having been told that Leonidas was king of Sparta and commander of the Spartan force, ordered his head to be cut off and fixed on a stake. This is in my opinion the strongest evidence—though there is plenty more—that King Xerxes, while Leonidas was still alive, felt fiercer anger against him than against any other man; had that not been so, he would never have committed this outrage upon his body; for normally the Persians, more than any other nation I know of, honour men who distinguish themselves in war. However, Xerxes' order was carried out.

I will now return to a point in my story where I omitted to mention something. The Spartans were the first to get the news that Xerxes was preparing an expedition against Greece; thereupon they sent to the Delphic oracle and received the answer of which I spoke a little while ago. The way they received the news was very remarkable: Demaratus, the son of Ariston, who was in exile in Persia, was not, I imagine—and as is only natural to suppose—well disposed towards the Spartans; so it is open to question whether what he did was inspired by benevolence or by malicious pleasure. Anyway, as soon as news reached him at Susa that Xerxes had decided upon the invasion of Greece, he felt that he must pass on the information to Sparta. As the danger of discovery was great, there was only one way in which he could contrive to get the message through: this was by scraping the wax off a pair of wooden folding tablets, writing on the wood underneath what Xerxes intended to do, and then covering the message over with wax again. In this way the tablets, being apparently blank, would cause no trouble with the guards along the road. When the message reached its destination, no one was able to guess the secret until, as I understand, Cleomenes' daughter Gorgo, who was the wife of Leonidas, divined it and told the others that, if they scraped the wax off, they would find something written on the wood underneath. This was done; the message was revealed and read, and afterwards passed on to the other Greeks. That, at any rate, is the story of what happened.

BOOK EIGHT

The following is the roll of the Greek naval force: 127 ships from Athens—partly manned by the Plataeans, whose courage and patriotism led them to undertake this service in spite of their ignorance of everything to do with the sea; 40 from Corinth, 20 from Megara, 20 more from Athens manned by crews from Chalcis, 18 from Aegina, 12 from Sicyon, 10 from Sparta, 8 from Epidaurus, 7 from Eretria, 5 from Troezen, 2 from Styra, and 2—together with two fifty-oared galleys—from Ceos. Lastly, the Locrians of Opus joined with seven fifty-oared galleys.

These, then, were the states which sent ships to Artemisium, and I have given the number which each contributed. The total strength of the fleet, excluding the small galleys, was thus 271 ships of war. The general officer in command, Eurybiades, the son of Eurycleides, was provided by Sparta; for the other members of the confederacy had stipulated for a Lacedaemonian commander, declaring that rather than serve under an Athenian they would break up the intended expedition altogether. From the first, even before Sicily was asked to join the alliance, there had been talk of the advisability of giving Athens command of the fleet; but the proposal had not been well received by the allied states, and the Athenians waived their claim in the interest of national survival, knowing that a quarrel about the command would certainly mean the destruction of Greece. They were, indeed, perfectly right; for the evil of internal strife is worse than united war in the same proportion as war itself is worse than peace. It was their realization of the danger attendant upon lack of unity which made them waive their claim, and they continued to do so as long as Greece desperately needed their help. This was made plain enough by their subsequent action; for when the Persians had been driven from Greece and the war had been carried to Persian territory, the Athenians made the insufferable behaviour of Pausanias their excuse for depriving the Lacedaemonians of the command.

When the Greeks on their arrival at Artemisium found a large Persian fleet lying at Aphetae and all the neighbourhood full of troops, it was evident to them that things had gone very differently with the Persians from what they had expected. They were seized by panic, and began to consider abandoning Artemisium and making their escape into the inner parts of Greece. This greatly alarmed the Euboeans, who no sooner realized what they had in mind than they begged Eurybiades to stay at any rate long enough to allow them to move their children and servants to a place of safety. Eurybiades refused, whereupon they went to Themistocles, the Athenian commander, and by a bribe of thirty talents induced him so to arrange matters that the Greek fleet should stay and fight on the coast of Euboea. The method Themistocles adopted to attain this object was to pass on to Eurybiades, as if it were a personal present from himself, a sixth part of the sum he had received from the Euboeans. This was enough to secure Eurybiades' consent; of the other commanders, however, there was still one who hesitated—Adeimantus son of Ocytus, the Corinthian, who declared that he would withdraw his ships from Artemisium. To him, therefore, Themistocles now addressed himself. "Never," he cried with an oath, "shall you leave us in the lurch! I will give you more for staying with us than the Persian king would ever send you

if you deserted us"; and without further delay he sent aboard
Adeimantus' ship three talents of silver. So Adeimantus and
Eurybiades yielded to bribery and the Euboeans' wishes were
gratified; Themistocles, too, made something out of the transaction, for he kept the rest of the money himself. Nobody knew
he had it, and the two men who had received their share imagined that it came from Athens especially for the purpose. These
were the circumstances which led to the Greeks engaging the
Persians on the Euboean coast, and I will now describe the battle
itself.

The Persians reached Aphetae early in the afternoon, and saw
for themselves what they had previously heard reported—namely
that a small Greek force was concentrated at Artemisium. At
once they were eager to engage, in the hope of capturing the
Greek ships. It did not, however, seem advisable to advance,
in the first instance, openly to the attack; for the Greeks, seeing
them coming, might try to escape, and then, when darkness
overtook them, they would be sure to get clear away. This would
not do, as the Persians were determined that not even a fire-
signaller (as they put it) must be allowed to escape alive. Laying
their plans accordingly, they detached a squadron of 200 ships
with orders to sail outside Sciathus, in order to escape enemy
observation, and then to turn southward round Euboea and into
the Euripus by way of Caphareus and Geraestus; in this way
they hoped to catch the Greeks in a trap, one squadron taking
them in the rear and blocking their retreat, the rest of the fleet
pressing upon them from in front. With this purpose in view
the two hundred ships were dispatched, while the main body
waited—for they did not intend to attack on that day, or until
they knew by signal that the squadron coming up the Euripus
had arrived. Meanwhile a review of the main fleet was held at
Aphetae, and while it was going on an interesting event occurred.
Serving with the Persian force there was a man named Scyllias,
a native of Scione and the most accomplished diver of his day,

who after the wreck of the Persian ships at Pelion had saved a great deal of valuable property for his masters—besides getting a good deal for himself. This man had apparently been thinking for some time past of deserting to the Greeks, but no opportunity had occurred until then. I cannot say for certain how it was that he managed to reach the Greeks, and the commonly accepted account is, at the least, doubtful; for, according to this, he dived under water at Aphetae and did not come up until he reached Artemisium—a distance of about ten miles. There are other somewhat tall stories, besides this, told about Scyllias—and also a few true ones; as to the one I have just related, my personal opinion is that he came to Artemisium in a boat. In any case, come he did; and on his arrival he lost no time in giving an account to the Greek commanders of all the circumstances of the disaster to the Persian fleet in the storm, and also told them about the squadron which was on its way round Euboea.

The Greek commanders at once proceeded to discuss the situation which this piece of intelligence produced; and after a long debate it was decided to stay where they were until after midnight, and then put to sea to meet the Persians who were coming up the Euripus. However, as time went on and they met with no opposition, they waited till the evening of the following day and then attacked the main enemy fleet, with the intention of testing Persian seamanship and tactics.

When the officers and men of Xerxes' fleet saw the Greeks moving to the attack with such a small force, they thought they were mad and at once got under way themselves, in confident expectation of making an easy capture; nor, indeed, was the expectation unreasonable, in view of the disparity in numbers —the Greek ships being few, and their own many times as numerous, as well as faster. Thus assured of their superiority, they developed a movement to surround the enemy. Those of the Ionians who had been forced to serve with the Persian fleet in spite of their real sympathy with the Greek cause were much distressed at the sight of the gradual encirclement of the Greeks, and convinced, in view of their apparent weakness, that not a man amongst them would escape alive; those, on the other hand, who welcomed the situation, entered into competition with each other to be the first to win a reward from Xerxes for the capture of an Athenian ship—for throughout the Persian fleet it was the Athenians who were most talked of.

At the first signal for action the Greek squadron formed into a close circle—bows outward, sterns to the centre; then, at the second signal, with little room to manoeuvre and lying, as they were, bows-on to the enemy, they set to work, and succeeded in capturing thirty Persian ships. Amongst the prisoners was Philaon, the son of Chersis and brother of Gorgus the king of Salamis, and a person of repute in the enemy force. The first Greek to take a prize was the Athenian Lycomedes, son of Aeschraeus. He was decorated for valour after the battle.

After this success, when darkness put an end to the fighting, the Greeks returned to Artemisium, and the Persians—who had had a considerable shock—to Aphetae. The only Greek in the Persian force to desert and join his countrymen during the action was Antidorus, the Lemnian; the Athenians afterwards showed their appreciation by giving him a grant of land in Salamis.

After dark—the season was midsummer—there was a very violent rainstorm, which lasted all night, accompanied by much thunder from the direction of Pelion. Dead bodies and bits of wreckage, drifting up to Aphetae, fell athwart the bows of the ships which lay there, and fouled the oar-blades of any that were under way; this, and the noise of the thunderstorm, caused a panic amongst the Persian troops, who began to think their last hour was come: they had, indeed, had much to put up with—for almost before they could draw breath again after the storm at Pelion, which wrecked so many of their ships, they were faced with a hard fight at sea, and now, on top of that, they were exposed to floods of rain, the rushing of swollen streams into the sea, and a tremendous thunderstorm.

For the Persians at Aphetae it was a bad enough night, but it was far worse for the squadron which had been ordered to sail round Euboea, for they were at sea when the storm caught them. Their fate was miserable: just as they were off the Hollows of Euboea the wind and rain began, and every ship, overpowered and forced to run blind before it, piled up on the rocks. Heaven was indeed doing everything possible to reduce the superiority of the Persian fleet and bring it down to the size of the Greek. So much for the disaster off the Hollows.

The Persians at Aphetae were very glad to see the dawn next morning, and did not feel like taking any further risks; it was enough for them, badly shaken as they were, to let the ships lie and attempt nothing for the present. Meanwhile the Greeks received a reinforcement of fifty-three ships from Athens; the arrival of this fresh squadron, together with the news of the loss in the storm of the whole Persian force which was sailing round Euboea, was a great encouragement, and the Greeks, on the strength of it, waiting till the same time as on the previous day, once again put to sea and attacked some Cilician vessels; these they destroyed and then, at the approach of darkness, they returned to Artemisium.

The Persian commanders were humiliated at receiving such rough treatment from so small a fleet; they were beginning, moreover, to be alarmed at the thought of what Xerxes might do to them; so on the third day they took the initiative, and, without waiting for the Greeks to move, made their preparations and put to sea round about midday. It so happened that these battles at sea took place on the same days as the battles at Thermopylae, and in each case the object was similar—to defend the passage into the heart of Greece: the fleet was fighting for the Euripus just as the army with Leonidas was fighting for the pass. So the Greek cry was to stop the enemy from getting through, while the Persians aimed at destroying the defending forces in order to clear the passage.

Xerxes' fleet now moved forward in good order to the attack, while the Greeks at Artemisium quietly awaited their approach. Then the Persians adopted a crescent formation and came on with the intention of surrounding their enemy, whereupon the Greeks advanced to meet them, and the fight began. In this engagement the two fleets were evenly matched—the Persian, by its mere size, proving its own greatest enemy, as constant confusion was caused by the ships fouling one another. Nonetheless they made a brave fight of it, to avoid the disgrace of defeat by so small an enemy force. The Greek losses both in ships and men were heavy, those of the Persians much heavier. Finally the action was broken off with such negative results as I have described. On the Persian side it was the Egyptians who came out of it with the best record, their most notable achievement being the capture of five Greek ships together with their crews; of the Greeks the most conspicuous were the Athenians—and in particular Cleinias, the son of Alcibiades, who was serving in his own ship manned by two hundred men, all at his own personal expense.

Both sides were glad when they parted and made all speed back to their moorings. The Greeks, once they were clear of the fighting, did, indeed, manage to possess themselves of the floating bodies and to salve the wreckage; nevertheless they had been so roughly handled—especially the Athenians, half of whose ships were damaged—that they determined to quit their station and withdraw further south. At this point it occurred to Themistocles that if the Ionian and Carian contingents could be detached from the Persian force, the Greeks would be able to deal successfully with the rest; accordingly he called his officers to a conference on the beach, to which the people of Euboea were already driving their sheep. Here he told them that he thought he had a plan, which might succeed in depriving Xerxes' fleet of its finest units. For the moment he gave no further details of what the plan was, but merely advised them, in view

of the circumstances, to slaughter as many of the Euboean sheep
as they pleased, as it was better that their own troops should
have them than the enemy. He further suggested that every
officer should order his men to light fires as usual; as for the
withdrawal from Artemisium, he made himself responsible for
choosing the proper moment and for seeing that they got home
safely. These proposals proved acceptable; so the commanders
at once had fires lighted, and the men set to on the cattle.

I should add here that the Euboeans had paid no attention
to the oracle of Bacis, supposing it to have no significance; they
had taken no precautions against the threat of war, either by
removing property from the island or by getting in stores, and
consequently found themselves in a highly dangerous position.
The oracle was as follows:

> When one of foreign speech casts a papyrus yoke upon the sea,
> Bethink you to keep the bleating goats far from Euboea.

This warning they ignored; and the result was great suffering,
both then and later, in the troubles which were daily expected.

While the Greeks were thus occupied, their observer arrived
from Trachis. The Greeks had employed two, to keep communication between the fleet and the army: at Artemisium Po-
lyas, a native of Anticyra, kept a boat ready to report to the
army at Thermopylae any reverse which might be suffered by
the fleet, while the Athenian Abronichus, the son of Lysides,
did similar duty with Leonidas, and had a thirty-oared galley
always available to report to Artemisium, if the army got into
any trouble. It was this Abronichus who now arrived with the
news of the fate of Leonidas and his men. The effect was immediate; the Greeks put off their withdrawal not a minute
longer, but got under way at once, one after another, the Corinthians leading, the Athenians bringing up the rear.

Themistocles took the fastest ships and called on the way at
all the places where drinking water was to be found, and cut

notices on the rocks nearby for the Ionians to read—as they did when they moved up on the following day. "Men of Ionia"— his message ran—"it is wrong that you should make war upon your fathers and help to bring Greeks into subjection. The best thing you can do is to join our side; if this is impossible, you might at least remain neutral, and ask the Carians to do the same. If you are unable to do either, but are held by a force so strong that it puts desertion out of the question, there is still another course open to you: in the next battle, remember that you and we are of the same blood, that our quarrel with Persia arose originally on your account—and fight badly."

In leaving this message Themistocles probably had two possibilities in mind: in the first place, it might, if the kings did not get to know of it, induce the Ionians to come over to the Greeks, and, secondly, if it were reported to Xerxes and made the ground of an accusation against the Ionians, they would be distrusted and not allowed, in consequence, to take part in engagements at sea.

Immediately after this a native of Histiaea sailed to Aphetae with the news of the Greek withdrawal from Artemisium. The Persians refused to believe it; they put the man under guard and sent off a party of some fast ships to see for themselves. Then, assured that the news was true, they moved at sunrise with the whole fleet to Artemisium, where they stayed until midday, before going on to Histiaea. They took this town, and overran all the coastal villages of Ellopia, a district belonging to Histiaea. While they were here, a messenger arrived from the king. Before sending him, Xerxes had arranged that of the twenty thousand men in the Persian army who had been killed at Thermopylae, all except about a thousand should be buried in trenches and covered over with earth and leaves, to prevent their being seen by anyone from the fleet. The remaining thousand were left exposed. On reaching Histiaea the messenger had the whole force assembled and delivered his message. "Friends and fellow-soldiers," he said, "the king grants leave for anyone who wants it, to go and see with his own eyes how he fights against the madmen who thought they could beat him." The announcement was no sooner made than so many people wanted to avail themselves of the king's offer that the supply of boats ran out. All who could, crossed the water and toured the battle-field to see the bodies; some of the corpses were, of course, those of helots, but the sightseers imagined that they were all Spartans and Thespians; however, Xerxes' ludicrous attempt to conceal the number of his own dead deceived nobody.

On the day after this, which had been spent in sight-seeing, the seamen rejoined their ships at Histiaea and the army with Xerxes set forward on its march. A few Arcadian deserters came in—men who had nothing to live on and wanted employment; they were taken to Xerxes and questioned about what the Greeks were doing. One Persian conducted the interrogation on behalf of them all, and he was told in reply that the Greeks were celebrating the Olympic festival, where they were watching ath-letic contests and chariot-races. When he asked what the prize was for which they contended, the Arcadians mentioned the wreath of olive-leaves which it is our custom to give. This drew from Tritantaechmes, the son of Artabanus, a very sound remark—though it made Xerxes call him a coward; for when he learned that the prize was not money but a wreath, he could not help crying out in front of everybody, "Good heavens, Mar-donius, what kind of men are these that you have brought us to fight against—men who compete with one another for no material reward, but only for honour!"

Meanwhile, immediately after the disaster at Thermopylae, the Thessalians sent a representative to Phocis. They had always been on bad terms with the Phocians, but especially so since the last blow they had received from them. Not many years before the Persian invasion they and their allies in full force had invaded Phocis and been defeated with serious losses. . . .

In addition to breaking out from Parnassus and inflicting this signal defeat on the Thessalian infantry, the Phocians also did irreparable damage to the Thessalian cavalry during an attempted raid. They dug a deep trench across the pass near Hyampolis, put a number of big empty jars in it, and covered them over lightly with soil; then, making the surface smooth and level to conceal the trap, they awaited the attack. The Thessalians galloped up, expecting to sweep all before them, when their horses fell through into the jars and broke their legs. Thus the Thessalians had two reasons for resentment when they sent their representative to Phocis. Their message ran as follows: "Men of Phocis, now at last you must admit your error, and own that you are not our equals. In the past, while it suited us to make one with the Greeks, we were always considered more important than you; and now our influence with the Persians is so great that a word from us would get you turned out of your country, and sold as slaves into the bargain. All the same, though we have you completely in our power, we are willing to let bygones be bygones: just pay us off with fifty talents, and we undertake to divert the danger which is threatening your country."

Now the Phocians were the only people in this part of Greece who had not gone over to the Persians, and in my opinion their motive was simply and solely their hatred of Thessaly. If Thessaly had remained loyal, no doubt the Phocians would have deserted to Persia. As it was, when they heard what the Thessalian representative had to say, they refused to pay a penny and declared that they could join Persia just as easily as the Thessalians did, had they been inclined that way; nevertheless, they would never willingly prove traitors to Greece. This reply to their message made the Thessalians very angry, and they forthwith offered to act as guides to the Persian army.

From Trachis the army entered the narrow strip of Dorian territory, barely four miles wide, which lies between Malis and

Phocis. . . . Passing from Doris into Phocis, they failed to catch the Phocians because they had already cleared out: some of them had gone up into the mountains—the height of Parnassus, called Tithorea, not far from Neon, has plenty of room for a large body of men, and a number of them had climbed up on to it and taken with them all they could move—while the majority had sought shelter with the Locrians of Ozolae and taken their property to Amphissa, the town which stands above the plain of Crisa. All Phocis was overrun; the Thessalians did not let the Persian army miss a bit of it, and everywhere they went there was devastation by fire and sword, and towns and temples were burnt. Along the valley of the Cephisus nothing was spared; Drymus, Charada, Erochus, Tethronium, Amphicaea, Neon, Pedies, Trites, Elateia, Hyampolis, Parapotamii—all these places were burnt to the ground, including Abae, where there was a temple of Apollo richly furnished with treasure and offerings of all kinds. There was an oracle there, as indeed there is to-day; the shrine belonging to it was plundered and burnt. A few Phocians were chased and caught near the mountains, and some women were raped successively by so many Persian soldiers that they died.

At Panopes, which they reached by way of Parapotamii, the army divided and one division, the stronger and more numerous, proceeded with Xerxes towards Athens, entering Boeotia near Orchomenus. All the Boeotians had gone over to the enemy, and their towns were protected by Macedonians, sent by Alexander, to make it clear to Xerxes that the people of Boeotia were friendly to him. The other division of the army made with their guides for the temple at Delphi, keeping Parnassus on their right. They, too, devastated all the parts of Phocis through which they passed, and burnt the towns of Panopes, Daulis, and Aeolidae. This division was detached from the main body of the army for the special purpose of plundering the temple at Delphi, and bringing its treasures to Xerxes; I have been told that he was better acquainted, from descriptions continually coming to his notice, with everything of importance there than with his own property at home, and especially with the precious objects which had been presented to the shrine by Croesus, the son of Alyattes.

The news of the approach of the Persians caused consternation at Delphi; and in their terror the people asked the God's advice as to whether they should bury the sacred treasures or get them out of the country. The God replied that they were not to be disturbed, for he was well able to guard his own. This being decided, the Delphians began to think about saving themselves; they sent their women and children across the water into Achaea, and most of the men took to the mountains in the summits of Parnassus, and stored their movable property in the Corycian cave, while a few of them made their escape to Amphissa in Locris. All abandoned the town except sixty men and the Priest of the oracle.

The Persians were now close at hand and within sight of the temple, when suddenly the Priest, whose name was Aceratus, saw weapons lying on the ground in front of the shrine—they were the sacred weapons which no human hand may touch, and they had been brought mysteriously out from their place within. He hastened to report this marvellous thing to the other Delphians who were still in the town. Meanwhile the enemy were drawing quickly nearer, and when they reached the temple of Athene Pronaea even stranger things happened to them than what I have just recorded. It is surprising enough that weapons of war should move of their own accord and appear upon the ground outside the shrine; but what occurred next is surely one of the most extraordinary things ever known—for just as the Persians came to the shrine of Athene Pronaea, thunderbolts fell on them from the sky, and two pinnacles of rock, torn from Parnassus, came crashing and rumbling down amongst them, killing a large number, while at the same time there was a battle-cry from inside the shrine. All these things happening together caused a panic amongst the Persian troops. They fled; and the Delphians, seeing them on the run, came down upon them and attacked them with great slaughter. All who escaped with their lives made straight for Boeotia. There is a story, I am told, amongst those who got away, that there was yet another miraculous occurrence: they saw, so they said, two gigantic soldiers—taller than ever a man was—pursuing them and cutting them down. According to the Delphians, these were Phylacus and Autonous, local heroes who have enclosed plots of ground near the temple, which are held sacred to them. . . .

The rocks which fell from Parnassus were still there in my time; they lay in the enclosure round the shrine of Pronaea, where they embedded themselves after crashing through the Persian troops. So that was how these people took their departure from the Holy Place at Delphi.

The Greek fleet, having sailed from Artemisium, brought up, at the Athenians' request, at Salamis. The Athenians' object in urging the commanders to take up this position was to give themselves an opportunity of getting their women and children out of Attica, and also of discussing their next move—as their present circumstances, and the frustration of their hopes, most evidently demanded. They had expected that the full strength of the Peloponnesian army would concentrate in Boeotia to hold up the Persian advance, but now they found nothing of the sort; on the contrary, they learned that the Peloponnesians were concerned only with their own safety and were fortifying the Isthmus in order to protect the Peloponnese, while the rest of Greece, so far as they cared, might take its chance. It was this news which led to the request to the fleet to put in at Salamis.

While, therefore, the rest of the fleet lay at Salamis, the Athenians returned to their own harbours, and at once issued a proclamation that everyone in the city and countryside should

get his children and all the members of his household to safety
as best he could. Most of them were sent to Troezen, but some
to Aegina and some to Salamis. The removal of their families
was pressed on with all possible speed, partly because they wished
to take the warning which had been given them by the oracle,
but more especially for an even stronger reason. The Athenians
say that the Acropolis is guarded by a great snake, which lives
in the temple; indeed they believed so literally in its existence
that they put out regular rations for it to eat in the form of a
honey-cake. Now in the past the honey-cake used always to be
consumed, but on this occasion it was untouched. The temple
Priestess told them of this, and in consequence, believing that
the goddess herself had abandoned the Acropolis, they were all
the more ready to evacuate the town. As soon as everything was
removed, they rejoined the fleet on its station.

There were some other Greek ships which had been ordered
to assemble at Pogon, the harbour of Troezen, and these, when
news came through that the fleet from Artemisium had put into
Salamis, left Troezen and joined it. Thus the fleet was larger
than it had been at the battle of Artemisium, and made up of
ships from more towns. It was still under the same commander,
Eurybiades, the son of Eurycleides—a Spartan but not of the
royal blood; but the city which furnished by far the greatest
number of ships, and the fastest, was Athens. The composition
of the fleet was as follows . . .

[Herodotus lists separately the number of warships contributed by
each of the Greek allies and calculates the total at 378, excluding
light galleys.]

When the commanders of the various contingents I have
mentioned met at Salamis, a council of war was held, and Eurybiades called for suggestions, from anyone who wished to speak,
on the most suitable place for engaging the enemy fleet in the

territory still under their control—Attica was excluded, as it had already been given up. The general feeling of the council was in favour of sailing to the Isthmus and fighting in defence of the Peloponnese, on the grounds that if they were beaten at Salamis they would find themselves blocked up in an island, where no help could reach them, whereas if disaster overtook them at the Isthmus, they could find refuge amongst their own people. This was the view of the Peloponnesian officers. While the discussion was still going on, a man arrived from Athens with the news that the Persians had entered Attica and were firing the whole country. This was the work of the division of the army under Xerxes which had taken the route through Boeotia; they had burnt Thespia after the inhabitants had escaped to the Peloponnese, and Plataea too, and then entered Attica, where they were causing wholesale devastation. The Thebans had told them that Thespia and Plataea had refused to submit to Persian domination: hence their destruction. The march of the Persian army from the Hellespont to Attica had taken three months—and the actual crossing of the strait an additional one; it reached Attica during the magistracy of Calliades.

The Persians found Athens itself abandoned except for a few people in the temple of Athene Polias—temple stewards and needy folk, who had barricaded the Acropolis against the invaders with planks and timbers. It was partly their poverty which prevented them from seeking shelter in Salamis with the rest, and partly their belief that they had discovered the real meaning of the Priestess' oracle—that "the wooden wall would not be taken." The wooden wall, in their minds, was not the ships but the barricade, and that would save them.

The Persians occupied the hill which the Athenians call the Areopagus, opposite the Acropolis, and began the siege. The method they used was to shoot into the barricade arrows with burning tow attached to them. Their wooden wall had betrayed them, but still the Athenians, though in imminent and deadly peril, refused to give in or even to listen to the proposals which the Pisistratidae made to them for a truce. All their ingenuity was employed in the struggle to defend themselves; amongst other things, they rolled boulders down the slope upon the enemy as he tried to approach the gates, and for a long time Xerxes was baffled and unable to take them. But in the end the Persians solved their problem: a way of access to the Acropolis was found—for it was prophesied that all Athenian territory upon the continent of Greece must be overrun by the Persians. There is a place in front of the Acropolis, behind the way up to the gates, where the ascent is so steep that no guard was set, because it was not thought possible that any man would be able to climb it; here, by the shrine of Cecrops' daughter Aglaurus, some soldiers managed to scramble up the precipitous face of the cliff. When the Athenians saw them on the summit, some leapt from the wall to their death, others sought sanctuary in the inner shrine of the temple; but the Persians who had got up first made straight for the gates, flung them open and slaughtered those in sanctuary. Having left not one of them alive, they stripped the temple of its treasures and burnt everything on the Acropolis. Xerxes, now absolute master of Athens, despatched a rider to Susa with news for Artabanus of his success.

On the following day he summoned to his presence the Athenian exiles who were serving with the Persian forces, and ordered them to go up into the Acropolis and offer sacrifice there according to Athenian usage; possibly some dream or other had suggested this course to him, or perhaps his conscience was uneasy for the burning of the temple. The Athenian exiles did as they were bidden. . . .

Meanwhile at Salamis the effect of the news of what had happened to the Acropolis at Athens was so disturbing, that some of the naval commanders did not even wait for the subject under discussion to be decided, but hurried on board and began hoisting sail for immediate flight. Some, however, stayed; and by these a resolution was passed to fight in defence of the Isthmus.

During the night, when the various commanders had returned on board after the break-up of the conference, an Athenian named Mnesiphilus made his way to Themistocles' ship and asked him what plan it had been decided to adopt. On learning that they had resolved to sail to the Isthmus and to fight there in defence of the Peloponnese, "No, no," he exclaimed; "once the fleet leaves Salamis, it will no longer be one country that you'll be fighting for. Everyone will go home, and neither Eurybiades nor anybody else will be able to prevent the total dissolution of our forces. The plan is absurd and will be the ruin of Greece. Now listen to me: try, if you possibly can, to upset the decision of the conference—it may be that you will be able to persuade Eurybiades to change his mind and remain at Salamis."

Themistocles highly approved of this suggestion, and without saying a word he went to the ship of the commander-in-chief and told him that he had something of public importance to discuss. Eurybiades invited him aboard and gave him permission to speak his mind, whereupon Themistocles, taking a seat beside him, repeated Mnesiphilus' arguments as if they were his own, with plenty of new ones added, until he convinced him, by the sheer urgency of his appeal, that the only thing to do was to go ashore and call the officers to another conference. The conference met, and then, before Eurybiades even had time to announce its purpose, Themistocles, unable to restrain his eagerness, broke into a passionate speech. He was interrupted by Adeimantus, the son of Ocytus, commander of the Corinthian contingent. "Themistocles," he observed, "in the races, the man who starts before the signal is whipped." "Yes," was Themistocles' retort, "but those who start too late win no prizes." It was a mild retort—for the moment. To Eurybiades he used none of his previous arguments about the danger of the force

breaking up if they left Salamis; for it would have been unbecoming to accuse any of the confederates actually to their
faces. The line he took this time was quite different. "It is now
in your power," he said, "to save Greece, if you take my advice
and engage the enemy's fleet here in Salamis, instead of withdrawing to the Isthmus as these other people suggest. Let me
put the two plans before you, and you can weigh them up and
see which is the better. Take the Isthmus first: if you fight there,
it will have to be in the open sea, and that will be greatly to
our disadvantage, with our smaller numbers and slower ships.
Moreover, even if everything else goes well, you will lose Salamis,
Megara, and Aegina. Again, if the enemy fleet comes south, the
army will follow it; so you will yourself be responsible for drawing it to the Peloponnese, thus putting the whole of Greece in
peril.

"Now for my plan: it will bring, if you adopt it, the following
advantages: first, we shall be fighting in narrow waters, and
there, with our inferior numbers, we shall win, provided things
go as we may reasonably expect. Fighting in a confined space
favours us but the open sea favours the enemy. Secondly, Salamis, where we have put our women and children, will be
preserved; and thirdly—for you the most important point of
all—you will be fighting in defence of the Peloponnese by remaining here just as much as by withdrawing to the Isthmus
—nor, if you have the sense to follow my advice, will you draw
the Persian army to the Peloponnese. If we beat them at sea,
as I expect we shall, they will not advance to attack you on the
Isthmus, or come any further than Attica; they will retreat in
disorder, and we shall gain by the preservation of Megara, Aegina, and Salamis—where an oracle has already foretold our
victory. Let a man lay his plans with due regard to common
sense, and he will usually succeed; otherwise he will find that
God is unlikely to favour human designs."

During his speech Themistocles was again attacked by the
Corinthian Adeimantus, who told him to hold his tongue

because he was a man without a country, and tried to prevent Eurybiades from putting any question to the vote at the instance of a mere refugee. Let Themistocles, he cried, provide himself with a country before he offered his advice. The point of the jibe was, of course, the fact that Athens had fallen and was in Persian hands. This time Themistocles' retort was by no means mild; he heartily abused both Adeimantus and the Corinthians, and made it quite plain that so long as Athens had two hundred warships in commission, she had both a city and a country much stronger than theirs—for there was not a single Greek state capable of repelling them, should they choose to attack.

With this he turned to Eurybiades again, and speaking more vehemently than ever, "As for you," he cried, "if you stay here and play the man—well and good; go, and you'll be the ruin of Greece. In this war everything depends upon the fleet. I beg you to take my advice; if you refuse, we will immediately put our families aboard and sail for Siris in Italy—it has long been ours, and the oracles have foretold that Athenians must live there some day. Where will you be without the Athenian fleet? When you have lost it you will remember my words."

This was enough to make Eurybiades change his mind; and no doubt his chief motive was apprehension of losing Athenian support, if he withdrew to the Isthmus; for without the Athenian contingent his strength would not have been adequate to offer battle. So he took the decision to stay where they were and fight it out at Salamis.

After these verbal skirmishes, when Eurybiades had made up his mind, they prepared to fight where they were. Day broke; just as the sun rose the shock of an earthquake was felt both on land and at sea, and the Greeks resolved to offer prayers to the gods and to call upon the Sons of Aeacus to fight at their side. As they resolved, so they did: they prayed to all the gods, and called upon Ajax and Telamon there in Salamis, and sent a ship to Aegina for Aeacus himself and his other Sons.

There is a story which used to be told by Dicaeus, the son of Theocydes, an Athenian exile who had some repute among the Persians. After the evacuation of Attica, when the Persian troops were devastating the countryside, he happened to be in the plain of Thria with Demaratus the Spartan. They saw a cloud of dust, such as might have been raised by an army of thirty thousand men on the march, coming from the direction of Eleusis, and were wondering what troops they could be, when they suddenly heard the sound of voices. Dicaeus thought he recognized the *Iacchus* song, which is sung at the Dionysiac mysteries, but Demaratus, who was unfamiliar with the religious ceremonial of Eleusis, asked his companion whose voices they were. "Sir," Dicaeus answered, "without any doubt some dreadful disaster is about to happen to the king's army. There is not a man left in Attica; so the voice we heard must clearly be a divine voice, coming from Eleusis to bring help to the Athenians and their friends. If it descends upon the Peloponnese, there will be danger for the king and for his army; if it moves towards the ships at Salamis, Xerxes may well lose his fleet. Every year the Athenians celebrate a festival in honour of the Mother and the Maid, and anyone who wishes, from Athens or elsewhere, may be initiated in the mysteries; the sound you heard was the Iacchus song which is always sung at that festival."

"Do not breathe a word of this to anybody," said Demaratus. "If it should reach the ears of the king, you would lose your head, and neither I nor anyone else in the world could save you. So hold your tongue—the gods will see to the king's army."

While Demaratus was speaking, the cloud of dust, from which the mysterious voice had issued, rose high into the air and drifted away towards Salamis, where the Greek fleet was stationed. By this the two men knew that the naval power of Xerxes was destined to be destroyed. Such was Dicaeus' story, and he used to appeal to Demaratus and others to witness the truth of it.

Meanwhile the Persian sailors had returned from Trachis to Histiaea after their sight-seeing tour of the battlefield, and three days later the fleet set sail. The ships passed through the Euripus, and in another three days arrived off Phaleron. In my judgment the Persian forces both by land and sea were just as strong at the time of their entry into Attica as they had been at Sepias and Thermopylae; for as an offset to the losses suffered in the storm, at Thermopylae, and at Artemisium, I reckon the reinforcements which had subsequently joined them. These were the Malians, Dorians, and Locrians; the Boeotians in full force except the Thespians and Plataeans; and in addition to these the Carystians, Andrians, Tenians, and all the other island peoples except the five whom I mentioned above. The further Xerxes advanced into Greece, the more peoples followed him.

All these troops came as far as Attica except the Parians, who stayed behind in Cythnus to watch the course of the war; and the rest of the fleet arrived, as I have said, at Phaleron. Here Xerxes paid it a personal visit, because he wished to talk to the commanding officers and hear their opinions; so when he had seated himself, the rulers of states and commanders of squadrons were summoned to appear before him, and took their seats according to the precedence which the king had assigned them—the lord of Sidon first, the lord of Tyre second, and so on in their order. Then, as they sat there in order of rank, Xerxes sent Mardonius to ask the opinion of each one about giving battle at sea. Mardonius accordingly went around putting his question, beginning with the lord of Sidon. The answers, with a single exception, were unanimously in favour of engaging the Greek fleet: the exception was Artemisia. "Mardonius," she said, "tell the king for me that this is the answer I give—I, whose courage and achievements in the battles at Euboea were surpassed by none: say to him, 'Master, my past services give me the right to advise you now upon the course which I believe to be most to your advantage. It is this: spare your ships and do not fight at sea, for the Greeks are as far superior to us in naval matters as men are to women. In any case, what pressing need have you to risk further actions at sea? Have you not taken Athens, the main objective of the war? Is not the rest of Greece in your power? There is no one now to resist you—those who did resist have fared as they deserved. Let me tell you how I think things will now go with the enemy; if only you are not in too great a hurry to fight at sea—if you keep the fleet on the coast where it now is—then, whether you stay here or advance into the Peloponnese, you will easily accomplish your purpose. The Greeks will not be able to hold out against you for long; you will soon cause their forces to disperse—they will soon break up and go home. I hear they have no supplies in the island where they now are; and the Peloponnesian contingents, at least, are not likely to be very easy in their minds if you march with the army towards their country—they will hardly like the idea of fighting in defence of Athens.

" 'If, on the other hand, you rush into a naval action, my fear is that the defeat of your fleet may involve the army too. And there is one other point, my lord, to be considered: good masters, remember, usually have bad servants, and bad masters good ones. You, then, being the best master in the world, are ill served: these people who are supposed to be your allies— these Egyptians, Cyprians, Cilicians, Pamphylians—are a useless lot!' "

Artemisia's friends were dismayed when they heard this speech, and thought that Xerxes would punish her for trying to dissuade him from battle; but those who were jealous of her standing among the most influential persons in the forces were delighted at the prospect of her ruin. However, when the several answers to his question were reported to the king, he was highly pleased with Artemisia's; he had always considered her an admirable person, but now he esteemed her more than ever. Nevertheless his orders were that the advice of the majority should be followed, for he believed that in the battles off Euboea his men had shirked their duty because he was not himself present — whereas this time he had made arrangements to watch the fight with his own eyes.

The command was now given to put to sea, and the ships proceeded towards Salamis, where they took up their respective stations at leisure. It was late in the evening, with not enough light left to attack at once; so they prepared to go into action next day.

The Greeks were in a state of acute alarm, especially those from the Peloponnese: for there they were, waiting at Salamis to fight for Athenian territory, and certain, in the event of defeat, to be caught and blocked up in an island, while their own country was left without defence, and the Persian army that very night was on the march for the Peloponnese.

Nevertheless everything that ingenuity could contrive had been done to prevent the Persian army from forcing the Isthmus. On the news of the destruction of Leonidas' force at Thermopylae, troops from all the states hurried to the Isthmus, where they took up their position under Cleombrotus, the son of Anaxandrides and brother of Leonidas. Their first act was to break up and block the Scironian Way; then, in accordance with a decision taken in council, they began work on a wall across the Isthmus. As there were many thousands there and every man turned to, the work went fast. Stones, bricks, timbers, sand-baskets — all were used in the building, and the labour went on continuously night and day. The peoples which joined in this work in full force were the following: Sparta, all the Arcadians, Elis, Corinth, Sicyon, Epidaurus, Phlius, Troezen, and Hermione: all these, in their overriding fear for the safety of Greece, helped in the work; but the other Peloponnesian communities (though the Olympic and Carneian festivals were now over) remained indifferent.

In the Peloponnese there are seven distinct peoples: two of them, the Arcadians and Cynurians, are indigenous; one, the

Achaeans, have always been in the Peloponnese, though they moved from their original territory; the four others—Dorians, Aetolians, Dryopes, and Lemnians—are immigrants.... Of these seven peoples all the communities except the ones I mentioned remained neutral in the war—which, to put it bluntly, is as good as saying that they were on the Persian side.

The Greeks at the Isthmus, convinced that all they possessed was now at stake and not expecting any notable success at sea, continued to grapple with their task of fortification. The news of how they were employed nevertheless caused great concern at Salamis; for it brought home to everyone there not so much his own peril as the imminent threat to the Peloponnese. At first there was whispered criticism of the incredible folly of Eurybiades; then the smothered feeling broke out into open resentment, and another meeting was held. All the old ground was gone over again, one side urging that it was useless to stay and fight for a country which was already in enemy hands, and that the fleet should sail and risk an action in defence of the Peloponnese, while the Athenians, Aeginetans, and Megarians still maintained that they should stay and fight at Salamis.

At this point Themistocles, feeling that he would be outvoted by the Peloponnesians, slipped quietly away from the meeting and sent a man over in a boat to the Persian fleet, with instructions upon what to say when he got there. The man—Sicinnus—was one of Themistocles' slaves and used to attend upon his sons; afterwards, when the Thespians were enrolling new citizens, Themistocles established him at Thespia and made him a rich man. Following his instructions, then, Sicinnus made his way to the Persian commanders and said: "I am the bearer of a secret communication from the Athenian commander, who is a well-wisher to your king and hopes for a Persian victory. He has told me to report to you that the Greeks are afraid and are planning to slip away. Only prevent them from slipping through your fingers, and you have at this moment an opportunity of unparalleled success. They are at daggers drawn with each other, and will offer no opposition—on the contrary, you will see the pro-Persians amongst them fighting the rest."

His message delivered, Sicinnus lost no time in getting away. The Persians believed what he had told them, and proceeded to put ashore a large force on the islet of Psyttaleia, between Salamis and the coast; then, about midnight, they moved their western wing in an encircling movement upon Salamis, while at the same time the ships off Ceos and Cynosura also advanced and blocked the whole channel as far as Munychia. The object of these movements was—ironically—that the Greeks might be cut off in Salamis and there give the Persians their revenge for the battles of Artemisium. The troops were landed on Psyttaleia because it lay right in the path of the impending action, and once the fighting began, many men and damaged vessels would be carried on to it, and could be saved or destroyed according as they were friends or enemies. These tactical moves were carried out in silence, to prevent the enemy from being aware of what was going on; they occupied the whole night, so that none of the men had time for sleep.

Now I cannot deny that there is truth in prophecies, and I have no wish to discredit them when they are expressed in unambiguous language. Consider the following:

> When they shall span the sea with ships from Cynosura
> To the holy shore of Artemis of the golden sword,
> Wild with hope at the ruin of shining Athens,
> Then shall bright Justice quench Excess, the child of Pride,
> Dreadful and furious, thinking to swallow up all things.
> Bronze shall mingle with bronze, and Ares with blood
> Incarnadine the sea; and all-seeing Zeus
> And gracious Victory shall bring to Greece the day of freedom.

With that utterance of Bacis in mind, absolutely clear as it is, I do not venture to say anything against prophecies, nor will I listen to criticism from others.

The Greek commanders at Salamis were still at loggerheads. They did not yet know that the enemy ships had blocked their escape at both ends of the channel, but supposed them to occupy the same position as they had seen them in during the day. However, while the dispute was still at its height, Aristides came over in a boat from Aegina. This man, an Athenian and the son of Lysimachus, had been banished from Athens by popular vote, but the more I have learned of his character, the more I have come to believe that he was the best and most honourable man that Athens ever produced. Arrived at Salamis, Aristides went to where the conference was being held and, standing outside, called for Themistocles. Themistocles was no friend of his; indeed he was his most determined enemy; but Aristides was willing, in view of the magnitude of the danger which threatened them, to forget old quarrels in his desire to communicate with him. He was already aware of the anxiety of the Peloponnesian commanders to withdraw to the Isthmus; as soon, therefore, as Themistocles came out of the conference in answer to his call, he said: "At this moment, more than ever before, you and I should be rivals, to see which of us can do most good to our country. First, let me tell you that the Peloponnesians may talk as much or as little as they please about withdrawing from Salamis—it will make not the least difference. What I tell you, I have seen with my own eyes: they *cannot* now get out of here, however much the Corinthians or Eurybiades himself may wish to do so, because our fleet is surrounded. So go in and tell them that!"

"Good news and good advice," Themistocles answered; "what I most wanted has happened—and you bring me the evidence of your own eyes that it is true. It was I who was responsible for this move of the enemy; for as our men would not fight here of their own free will, it was necessary to make them, whether they wanted to do so or not. But take them the good news yourself; if I tell them, they will think I have invented it and will not believe me. Please, then, go in and make the report yourself. If they believe you, well and good; if they do not, it's no odds; for if we are surrounded, as you say we are, escape is no longer possible.''

Aristides accordingly went in and made his report, saying he had come from Aegina and had been hard put to it to slip through the blockading enemy fleet, as the entire Greek force was surrounded. He advised them, therefore, to prepare at once to repel an attack. That said, he left the conference, whereupon another dispute broke out, because most of the commanders still refused to believe in the report. But while they still doubted, a Tenian warship, commanded by Panaetius, the son of Sosimenes, deserted from the Persians and came in with a full account. . . .

Forced to accept the Tenians' report, the Greeks now at last prepared for action. At dawn the fighting men were assembled and Themistocles was chosen to address them. The whole burden of what he said was a comparison of all that was best and worst in life and fortunes, and an exhortation to the men to choose the better. Then, having rounded off his speech, he gave the order for embarkation. The order was obeyed and, just as the men were going aboard, the ship which had been sent to Aegina to fetch the Sons of Aeacus, rejoined the fleet.

The whole fleet now got under way, and in a moment the Persians were on them. The Greeks checked their way and began to back astern; and they were on the point of running aground when Ameinias of Pallene, in command of an Athenian ship, drove ahead and rammed an enemy vessel. Seeing the two ships foul of one another and locked together, the rest of the Greek fleet hurried to Ameinias' assistance, and the general action began. Such is the Athenian account of how the battle started; the Aeginetans claim that the first to go into action was the ship which fetched the Sons of Aeacus from Aegina. There is also a popular belief that the phantom shape of a woman appeared and, in a voice which could be heard by every man in the fleet, contemptuously cried out: "Fools, how much further do you propose to go astern?"

The Athenian squadron found itself facing the Phoenicians, who formed the Persian left wing on the western, Eleusis, end of the line; the Lacedaemonians faced the ships of Ionia, which were stationed on the Piraeus, or eastern, end. A few of the Ionians remembered Themistocles' appeal and deliberately held back in the course of the fighting; but most, not at all. . . .

The greater part of the Persian fleet suffered severely in the battle, the Athenians and Aeginetans accounting for a great many of their ships. Since the Greek fleet worked together as a whole, while the Persians had lost formation and were no longer fighting on any plan, that was what was bound to happen. None the less they fought well that day—far better than in the actions off Euboea. Every man of them did his best for fear of Xerxes, feeling that the king's eye was on him.

I cannot give precise details of the part played in this battle by the various Greek or foreign contingents in the Persian fleet; I must, however, mention Artemisia, on account of an exploit which still further increased her reputation with Xerxes. After the Persian fleet had lost all semblance of order, Artemisia was chased by an Athenian trireme. As her ship happened to be closest to the enemy and there were other friendly ships just ahead of her, escape was impossible. In this awkward situation she hit on a plan which turned out greatly to her advantage: with the Athenian close on her tail she drove ahead with all possible speed and rammed one of her friends—a ship of Calynda, with Damasithymus, the Calyndian king, on board. I cannot say if she did this deliberately because of some quarrel she had had with this man while the fleet was in the Hellespont, or if it was just chance that that particular vessel was in her way; but in any case she rammed and sank her, and was lucky enough, as a result, to reap a double benefit. For the captain of the Athenian trireme, on seeing her ram an enemy, naturally supposed that her ship was a Greek one, or else a deserter which was fighting on the Greek side; so he abandoned the chase and turned to attack elsewhere. That, then, was one piece of luck —that she escaped with her life; the other was that, by this very act she raised herself higher than ever in Xerxes' esteem. For the story goes that Xerxes, who was watching the battle, observed the incident, and that one of the bystanders remarked: "Do you see, my lord, how well Artemisia is fighting? She has sunk an enemy ship." Xerxes asked if they were sure it was really Artemisia, and was told that there was no doubt whatever—they knew her ensign well, and of course supposed that it was an enemy ship that had been sunk. She was, indeed, lucky in every way—not least in the fact that there were no survivors from the Calyndian ship to accuse her. Xerxes' comment on what was told him is said to have been: "My men have turned into women, my women into men."

Amongst the killed in this struggle was Ariabignes, the son of Darius and Xerxes' brother, and many other well-known men from Persia, Media, and the confederate nations. There were also Greek casualties, but not many; for most of the Greeks could swim, and those who lost their ships, provided they were not killed in the actual fighting, swam over to Salamis. Most of the enemy, on the other hand, being unable to swim, were drowned. The greatest destruction took place when the ships which had been first engaged turned tail; for those astern fell foul of them in their attempt to press forward and do some service before the eyes of the king. In the confusion which resulted, some Phoenicians who had lost their ships came to Xerxes and tried to make out that the loss was due to the treachery of the Ionians. But the upshot was that it was they themselves, and not the Ionian captains, who were executed for misbehaviour. While they were speaking, a ship of Samothrace rammed an Athenian; the Athenian was going down, when an

Aeginetan vessel bore down upon the Samothracian and sank her, but the Samothracian crew, who were armed with javelins, cleared the deck of the attacking vessel, leapt aboard, and captured her. This exploit saved the Ionians; for when Xerxes saw an Ionian ship do such a fine piece of work, he turned to the Phoenicians and, ready as he was in his extreme vexation to find fault with anyone, ordered their heads to be cut off, to stop them from casting cowardly aspersions upon their betters.

Xerxes watched the course of the battle from the base of Mt. Aegaleos, across the strait from Salamis; whenever he saw one of his officers behaving with distinction, he would find out his name, and his secretaries wrote it down, together with his city and parentage.

The Persian Ariaramnes, who was a friend of the Ionians and was present during the battle, also had a share in bringing about the punishment of the Phoenicians.

When the Persian rout began and they were trying to get back to Phalerum, the Aeginetan squadron, which was waiting to catch them in the narrows, did memorable service. The enemy was in hopeless confusion; such ships as offered resistance or tried to escape were cut to pieces by the Athenians, while the Aeginetans caught those which attempted to get clear, so that any ship which escaped the one enemy promptly fell amongst the other. . . .

Such of the Persian ships as escaped destruction made their way back to Phalerum and brought up there under the protection of the army.

The most distinguished service at Salamis is admitted to have been that of Aegina; and next after Aegina was Athens. The greatest individual distinction was won by Polycritus of Aegina, and the two Athenians, Eumenes of Anagyrus and Ameinias of Pallene. It was Ameinias who gave chase to Artemisia, and if he had known that Artemisia was on board, he would never have abandoned the chase until he had either taken her or been taken himself; for the Athenians resented the fact that a woman should appear in arms against them, and the ships' captains had received special orders about her, with the offer of a reward of 10,000 drachmae for anyone who captured her alive. However, as I said, she escaped; some others, too, got away with their ships, and these now lay at Phalerum. . . .

During the confused struggle a valuable service was performed by the Athenian Aristides, son of Lysimachus, whose high character I remarked upon a little while back. He took a number of the Athenian heavy infantry, who were posted along the coast of Salamis, across to Psyttaleia, where they killed every one of the Persian soldiers who had been landed there.

After the battle the Greeks towed over to Salamis all the disabled vessels which were adrift in the neighbourhood, and then prepared for a renewal of the fight, fully expecting that Xerxes would use his remaining ships to make another attack. Many of the disabled vessels and other wreckage were carried by the westerly wind to a part of the Attic coast called Colias, and in this way it came about that not only the prophecies of Bacis and Musaeus about this battle were fulfilled, but also another prophecy which had been uttered many years previously by an Athenian soothsayer named Lysistratus: the words of this one were, "The Colian women shall cook their food with oars." The Greeks had forgotten about it at the time, but it was to happen, all the same, after Xerxes was gone.

Xerxes, when he realized the extent of the disaster, was afraid that the Greeks, either on their own initiative or at the suggestion of the Ionians, might sail to the Hellespont and break the bridges here. If this happened, he would be cut off in Europe and in danger of destruction. Accordingly, he laid his plans for escape; but at the same time, in order to conceal his purpose both from the Greeks and from his own troops, he began to construct a causeway across the water towards Salamis, lashing together a number of Phoenician merchantmen to serve at once for bridge and breakwater. He also made other preparations, as if he intended to fight again at sea. The sight of this activity made everybody confident that he was prepared to remain in Greece and carry on the war with all possible vigour; there was, however, one exception—Mardonius, who thoroughly understood how his master's mind worked and was in no way deceived. At the same time Xerxes dispatched a courier to Persia with the news of his defeat. . . .

Xerxes' first dispatch telling of the capture of Athens caused such rejoicing in Susa amongst the Persians who had not accompanied the expedition, that they strewed the roads with myrtle-boughs, burned incense, and gave themselves up to every sort of pleasure and merrymaking; the second, however, coming on top of it, soon put a stop to all this, and such was the distress in the city that there was not a man who did not tear his clothes and weep and wail in unappeasable grief, laying the blame for the disaster upon Mardonius. Nor was it distress for the loss of the ships which caused these demonstrations; it was fear for the personal safety of the king. The demonstrations, moreover, continued without a break until Xerxes himself came home.

Mardonius could see that Xerxes took the defeat at Salamis very hard, and guessed that he had determined to get out of Athens. In these circumstances, reckoning that he was sure to be punished for having persuaded the king to undertake the expedition, he felt it would be better to renew the struggle in order either to bring Greece into subjection or, failing that, to die nobly in a great cause—though he expected the former alternative. Accordingly, he approached Xerxes with a proposal. "My lord," he said, "I beg you not to take recent events too deeply to heart. What are a few planks and timbers? The decisive struggle will not depend upon them, but upon men and horses. Not one of all these people who now imagine that their work is done, will dare leave his ship in order to oppose you, nor will the mainland Greeks—those who have done so already have paid the price. I suggest, therefore, an immediate attack upon the Peloponnese. Or wait a while, if you prefer. In any case do not lose heart; for the Greeks cannot possibly escape ultimate subjection. They will be brought to account for the injuries they have done you, now and in the past. That is your best policy; nevertheless I have another plan to offer, should you be determined to withdraw the army from Greece. My lord, do not give the Greeks the chance to laugh at us. None of the reverses we have suffered have been due to us—you cannot say that we Persians have on any occasion fought like cowards. Why should we care if the Egyptians and Phoenicians and Cyprians and Cilicians have disgraced themselves? Persia is not involved in their disgrace. No; it is not we who are responsible for what has occurred. Listen, then, to what I have to propose; if you have made up your mind not to stay here, then go home together with the greater part of the army, and I will make it my duty, with 300,000 picked troops, to deliver Greece to you in chains.''

The proposal was welcome to Xerxes in his dejection; he was highly delighted, and told Mardonius that he would consider the two alternatives and let him know which he preferred to adopt. Accordingly he summoned a conference, and during the debate it occurred to him that it would be just as well to send for Artemisia to take part in the discussion, as she on a previous occasion had been the only one to give him sound advice. When she presented herself, Xerxes dismissed his Persian advisers, and all the guards, and addressed her in these words:

"Mardonius urges me to stay in Greece and attack the Peloponnese. According to him, my army and my Persian troops, who have not been responsible for any of our recent disasters, are anxious to prove their worth. His advice, therefore, is, either that I should undertake this campaign, or allow him to choose 300,000 men from the army and lead the expedition himself, while I return home with the remainder of my troops. With that force he promises to deliver Greece into my hands. You gave me good advice when you tried to dissuade me from risking the battle we have just fought at sea; so I would ask you to advise me now. Which of these two courses should I be wise to follow?"

"My lord," Artemisia answered, "it is not easy to give you the best advice; nevertheless, circumstances being as they are, I think that you should yourself quit this country and leave Mardonius behind with the force he asks for, if that is what he wants, and if he has really undertaken to do as he has said. If his design prospers and success attends his arms, it will be *your* work, master—for your slaves performed it. And even if things go wrong with him, it will be no great matter, so long as you yourself are safe and no danger threatens anything that concerns your house. While you and yours survive, the Greeks will have to run many a painful race for their lives and land; but who cares if Mardonius comes to grief? He is only your slave, and the Greeks will have but a poor triumph if they kill him. As for yourself, you will be going home with the object of your campaign accomplished—for you have burnt Athens."

Artemisia's advice was most agreeable to Xerxes, for it was the expression of his own thoughts. Personally, I do not think he would have stayed in Greece, had all his counsellors, men and women alike, urged him to do so—he was much too badly frightened. As it was, he complimented Artemisia and sent her off to Ephesus with his sons—some of his bastards which had accompanied him on the expedition. . . .

Xerxes, having entrusted Artemisia with the duty of conducting his bastard sons to Ephesus, sent for Mardonius and told him to pick the troops he wanted, and to take care to make his deeds answer to his words. That day nothing further was done; but the same night the king gave his orders, and the fleet slipped away from Phalerum, the commander of every vessel making the best speed he could across to the Hellespont, in order to guard the bridges for Xerxes' use on his return. Off

Zoster, where some little rocky headlands run out from the coast, the Persians mistook the rocks for enemy ships and gave them a very wide berth; however, they realized their mistake after a time, and continued the voyage in company.

At dawn the following day the Greeks, seeing that the Persian army had not moved, thought that the fleet would still be lying at Phalerum; so they prepared to defend themselves in expectation of another attack by sea. But the moment they learnt that the fleet was gone, they resolved to give chase, and did actually sail in pursuit as far as Andros, but without getting a sight of any enemy ships. At Andros they brought up and held a conference, at which Themistocles proposed that they should carry on through the islands direct for the Hellespont, and break the bridges. Eurybiades, however, objected, on the ground that to destroy the bridges would be to do Greece the worst possible service. If, he argued, Xerxes were cut off from home and forced to stay in Greece, he would hardly be likely to remain inactive. Inactivity would ruin all his chances of success and rob him of any opportunity of getting home again, and his troops would starve; whereas if he took the offensive and acted with vigour, the whole of Europe might gradually go over to him; for the various towns and peoples would, one by one, either be beaten in the field or agree to submit; moreover, the annual harvests would allow his troops to live off the country. Therefore, as Xerxes evidently intended, in consequence of his defeat at Salamis, not to remain in Greece, he should be allowed to make his escape back to his own country; and then, Eurybiades concluded, the war could be transferred to Asia.

Eurybiades was supported in his view by the other Peloponnesian commanders, whereupon Themistocles, finding the majority against him, suddenly shifted his ground and addressed himself to the Athenians—who of all the confederates were the most vexed at the enemy's escape, and were anxious to go on to the Hellespont alone, if the others refused to accompany them.

"From my own experience," Themistocles began, "and still more from what others have told me, I know very well that people who are beaten and cornered will often hit out again and make amends for their previous failure to play the man. Now we've had the luck to save ourselves and our country by the repulse of this great force, which seemed, like a cloud, to darken the sea. That force is now in flight—let it go. Indeed it was not we who performed this exploit; it was God and our divine protectors, who were jealous that one man in his godless pride should be king of Asia and of Europe too—a man who does not know the difference between sacred and profane, who burns and destroys the statues of the gods, and dared to lash the sea with whips and bind it with fetters. At the moment, all is well with us; so let us stay where we are, in our own country, and look after ourselves and our families. The Persians are gone— flung out, once and for all; so repair your houses, every one of you, and attend to the sowing of your land. We can sail for the Hellespont and Ionia next spring."

Themistocles' idea in saying this was to lay the foundation for a future claim upon Xerxes, in order to have somewhere to turn to in the event—which did in fact occur—of his getting into trouble with the Athenians. But whatever his ulterior motives, the Athenians were ready to take his advice; they had always thought him clever, and now that he had proved beyond a doubt both clever and successful, they were willing to follow his lead in everything.

Once he had persuaded them to accept his proposal, Themistocles lost no time in getting a message through to Xerxes. The men he chose for this purpose were all people he could trust to keep his instructions secret, even under torture. One of them, as on a previous occasion, was his servant Sicinnus. The party crossed to Attica, and then, while the others waited by the boat, Sicinnus went to find Xerxes, and deliver his message. "I have come," he said, "on behalf of Themistocles, son of

Neocles and commander of the Athenian fleet, the most brilliant leader of the confederacy. I am to inform you that Themistocles of Athens, in his desire to serve your interests, has stopped the Greeks from pursuing your navy and destroying the bridges on the Hellespont, which is what they wished to do. You may now, therefore, march your army home without danger of interference."

The message delivered, the men returned to Andros; and the Greeks, now that it was decided neither to continue the chase nor to sail to the Hellespont to break the bridges, invested the city with the intention of taking it. The Andrians were the first of the islanders to refuse Themistocles' demand for money; he had put it to them that they would be unable to avoid paying, because the Athenians had the support of two powerful deities, one called Persuasion and the other Compulsion, and the Andrians had replied that Athens was lucky to have two such useful gods, who were obviously responsible for her wealth and greatness; unfortunately, however, they themselves, in their small and inadequate land, had two utterly useless deities, who refused to leave the island and insisted on staying; and their names were Poverty and Inability. With the support of these, no money would be forthcoming; for however strong Athens was, she could never turn Andros' "can't" into "can." This answer, and the refusal to pay, were the reasons for the siege.

Meanwhile Themistocles, always greedy for money, sent demands to the other islands; he employed the same messengers as he had sent to Xerxes, and backed his demand by the threat that, if they did not pay what he asked, he would bring the Greek fleet and blockade them into surrender. By these means he succeeded in collecting large sums from the people of Carystos and Paros, who took fright and paid up when they heard that Andros was already invested because of her support of Persia, and that Themistocles had the highest reputation of the Greek commanders. I cannot say whether or not any of the other islanders gave Themistocles money—though they probably did. The Carystians got no benefit from their compliance; the Parians, however, having thus propitiated Themistocles, escaped a visit from the fleet. Thus it was that Themistocles extorted money from the islanders, while he lay at Andros. The other commanders knew nothing of these proceedings.

A few days after the battle of Salamis, Xerxes' army began its withdrawal, marching into Boeotia by the same route as it had taken during its advance. Mardonius wished to accompany the king for part of his way home, and, as it was not then the campaigning season, he judged that it would be better to winter in Thessaly and make his attempt upon the Peloponnese the following spring. On his arrival there he chose the troops which were to serve under his command. . . .

While Xerxes was in Thessaly and Mardonius was selecting the troops for his army, the Lacedaemonians received a message from the oracle at Delphi, urging them to demand reparation from Xerxes for the killing of Leonidas, and to accept whatever he offered them. The Spartans at once sent a representative, who was in time to catch the Persian army before it left Thessaly. The man obtained an interview with Xerxes, and said: "My lord King of the Medes, the Lacedaemonians and the house of Heracles in Sparta demand satisfaction for blood, because you killed their king while he was fighting in defence of Greece." Xerxes laughed, and for a time did not answer; then, pointing to Mardonius who happened to be standing by him, "They will get," he said, "all the satisfaction they deserve from Mardonius here." The messenger accepted this for an answer and went home.

Xerxes now left Mardonius in Thessaly and made his way by forced marches to the Hellespont. He reached the crossing in forty-five days, but with hardly a fraction of his army intact. During the march the troops lived off the country as best they could, eating grass where they found no grain, and stripping the bark and leaves off trees of all sorts, cultivated or wild, to stay their hunger. They left nothing anywhere, so hard were they put to it for supplies. Plague and dysentery attacked them; many died, and others who fell sick were left behind in the various towns along the route, with instructions for their care and keep—some in Thessaly, others at Siris in Paeonia, others in Macedon. . . .

The Persians, having passed through Thrace, reached the passage over the Hellespont and lost no time in getting across to Abydos. They crossed, however, in ships, as they found the bridges no longer in position, but shattered by storms. Food was more plentiful at Abydos than what they had had on the march, with the result that the men over-ate themselves, and this, combined with the change of water, caused many deaths in what remained of the army. The remnant proceeded with Xerxes to Sardis. . . .

The Greeks, meanwhile, failed to take Andros and turned their attention to Carystos. They devastated its land, and then returned to Salamis. Their first act on reaching Salamis was to choose from the plunder taken in the battle the "first fruits" to be offered in token of gratitude to the gods; these consisted of various objects, but most notably of three Phoenician warships, one to be dedicated at the Isthmus (where it was still to be seen in my own day), another at Sunium, and another, as an offering to Ajax, in Salamis itself. They then turned to the division of the plunder, and sent to Delphi the "first fruits" set apart for the purpose. . . .

After the dispatch of the thank-offerings to Delphi, the Greeks asked the god, in the name of the country generally, if he felt he had received his full share and was satisfied. His answer was that he was satisfied with what everyone had given, except the Aeginetans: from them he demanded his due from their prize of valour won at Salamis. In consequence of this the Aeginetans dedicated the three gold stars on a bronze mast—now to be seen in the corner near the bowl which was dedicated by Croesus. When the plunder had been distributed, the Greeks sailed to the Isthmus, where a prize of valour was to be awarded to the man who was judged best to deserve it by his conduct throughout the campaign. The commanders met at the altar of Poseidon to cast their votes for first and second place; and, as they all thought that they had fought more bravely than anybody else, every one of them put his own name at the top—though the majority agreed in putting Themistocles second. Consequently nobody got more than one vote for first place, while Themistocles easily headed the poll for the second. Mutual jealousy thus prevented a decision, and the various commanders sailed off home without making an award; in spite of this, however, Themistocles' name was on everyone's lips, and he acquired the reputation of being by far the most able man in the country.

Immediately after this, having failed to win from the men who fought at Salamis the mark of honour to which he was entitled, he went to Lacedaemon hoping for honour there. He was given a splendid welcome, and treated with the highest respect. The actual prize of valour—a wreath of olive—was, indeed, given to Eurybiades, but a similar wreath was granted to Themistocles as well, for his ability and skill. He was also presented with a chariot, the finest in Sparta, and received high praise. On his departure he was escorted as far as the borders of Tegea by the picked troop of three hundred Spartans called the Knights. Themistocles was the only person we know of who ever received the honour of an escort from the Spartans. . . .

Artabazus . . . , who was already a famous man in the Persian army and was further to increase his reputation as a result of the battle of Plataea, acted as escort to Xerxes, with 60,000 of

Mardonius' picked troops, as far as the crossing over the Hellespont. Once the king was in Asia, Artabazus set out on his march back; realizing on his arrival in the neighbourhood of Pallene that Mardonius was wintering in Thessaly and Macedonia, and being as yet in no hurry to rejoin the rest of the army, he considered it his duty, as he found Potidaea in a state of revolt, to bring the town into subjection. The people of Potidaea, like the other inhabitants of the Pallene peninsula, had openly thrown off the Persian yoke as soon as Xerxes passed them on his march to the eastward and they knew of the flight of the Persian fleet from Salamis.

Artabazus, therefore, began the siege, and at the same time invested Olynthus in expectation of a similar revolt. . . . The town soon fell; Artabazus butchered the inhabitants and threw their bodies into a lake, turning over the town itself to the control of Critobulus of Torone and the Chalcidians—which was how these people got possession of Olynthus. Artabazus then turned all his attention to Potidaea. . . .

Three months later, while the siege was still in progress, there was an exceptionally low tide which lasted a long time. The sight of the shallow water suggested to the Persians the possibility of getting through it and across into Pallene. But when they were two-fifths of the way over, they were caught by the succeeding flood, which was of corresponding height—indeed, according to the people thereabouts, higher than it had been before, though big tides are not uncommon there. All the men who could not swim were drowned, and those who could were killed by the Potidaeans, who went out after them in boats. This excessive tide and the consequent disaster to the Persians are put down by the people of Potidaea to the fact that the men who met their deaths were the same ones as had previously desecrated the shrine of Poseidon, and the statue of him which stands just outside the town. Personally, I think their explanation is the true one. After this incident Artabazus withdrew with the remainder of his men and rejoined Mardonius in Thessaly.

The surviving ships of Xerxes' fleet, having made good their escape from Salamis to Asia, had ferried the king and the army across the strait from the Chersonese to Abydos, and then laid up for the winter at Cyme. . . . The fact is that, so far as naval operations were concerned, the Persians had completely lost heart, though they still believed that Mardonius and his army were sure of an easy victory. Accordingly they kept the fleet at Samos, laying plans for any possible means of harassing the enemy, and at the same time waiting for news of Mardonius.

The coming of spring and the presence of Mardonius in Thessaly roused the Greeks to action again. Before the army mustered, the fleet, 110 strong, proceeded to Aegina under the supreme command of Leotychides. Leotychides belonged to the younger branch of the Spartan royal house, and traced his descent back to Heracles. . . . The Athenian squadron was commanded by Xanthippus, the son of Ariphron.

After the arrival of the fleet at Aegina, representatives from Ionia—amongst them Herodotus, the son of Basileides—came to the Greek headquarters with a request for aid. They were the same men as had visited Sparta not long before to ask the Spartans to liberate Ionia. Originally there were seven of them, and they had formed a conspiracy to murder Strattis, the master of Chios; but the plot was betrayed by one of their number, and the remaining six left the island and went to Sparta; and after that, as I have said, they came on to Aegina with a request to the Greeks to undertake an expedition to Ionia. However, it was only with great difficulty that they persuaded them to advance as far as Delos, for the Greeks had little experience of what lay beyond, and imagined it to be full of Persian troops and of every sort of danger. As for Samos, it seemed to them as far away as the Pillars of Heracles. The result was that while the Persians were too badly scared to risk sailing west of Samos, the Greeks, in spite of the earnest solicitation of the Chians, did not dare to sail east of Delos. Their mutual fears stood sentry over the intervening area.

While Mardonius was wintering in Thessaly, he instructed a man named Mys, a Carian from the town of Euromus, to make the round of all the oracles which it was possible for him to consult. What precisely he hoped to learn from the oracles when he gave this order, I cannot say, for there is no record; but presumably he sent for information and advice on the business he had at the moment in hand, and not for any other purpose. . . . Mardonius read whatever it was the oracle said, and then sent Alexander, the son of Amyntas, to Athens with a message. He chose Alexander, who was a Macedonian, for two reasons: first, because he was connected with the Persians by marriage . . . , [and] secondly, because he was well aware that Alexander's friendship with Athens was an official relationship, and was backed by deeds. Mardonius therefore thought that by sending him he would be most likely to bring Athens over to the Persian interest; he knew that the Athenians were a numerous and gallant people, and had been chiefly responsible for the defeat of the Persian navy, and expected that if only he could form an alliance with them, he would have no difficulty in getting the mastery of the sea—an expectation which was per-fectly justified—while he was already confident of his superiority on land. In this way he reckoned that the defeat of Greece would be within his grasp. For all I know, the Athenian alliance had been what the oracles advised, and it was in obedience to them that he sent Alexander on his mission. . . .

On his arrival at Athens as Mardonius' ambassador, Alex-ander spoke in the following terms: "Men of Athens, this is from Mardonius: I have received a message from the king, which says: 'I am willing to forget all the injuries which Athens had done me. So, Mardonius, first give the Athenians back their land; and secondly, let them take whatever other territory they wish, and have self-government. If they are willing to come to terms with me, you are also to rebuild the temples which I burnt.' Those are the King's orders which I have to carry out, unless you yourselves put obstacles in the way. Why then—I ask you—are you so mad as to take arms against the king? You can never defeat him, and you cannot hold out for ever. You have seen his army, its size, and what it can do; you know, too, how powerful a force I have under me now. Even should you beat us—and, if you have any sense, you cannot hope to do so—another force many times as powerful will come against you. So stop trying to be a match for the king, at the cost of the loss of your country and continual peril of your lives. Come to terms with him instead—you have the finest possible opportunity of doing so, now that Xerxes is inclined that way. Make an alliance with us, with every usual guarantee against aggression, and so keep your freedom.

"So much for what Mardonius instructed me to say to you. Now let me speak for myself. There is no need to mention my goodwill towards you—that you already know well enough; I merely add my earnest entreaties that you will do as Mardonius asks. It is clear to me that you will not be able to maintain your struggle with Xerxes forever—had I thought you could, I should never have come to Athens on this mission. But the fact is, Xerxes' power is superhuman, and his arm is long. If, then, you do not at once conclude a peace, now that such excellent terms are offered, I tremble for your future, when I think how of all the confederate states you lie most directly in the path of danger. You alone will continue to suffer, since your country will be a sort of no-man's-land. Do, therefore, agree; for surely it is no small thing that the Great King should single you out from all the people of Greece, and be willing to forgive the past and to become your friend."

In Sparta the news of Alexander's visit to try to bring about an alliance between Persia and Athens caused consternation. The Spartans, remembering the prophecy that the Dorians would one day be expelled from the Peloponnese by the Persians and Athenians, and greatly fearing that the alliance might be concluded, at once decided to send representatives to Athens. It so happened that Alexander and the Spartan envoys had their audience at the same time; for the Athenians had dragged out their business with Alexander, realizing that the Spartans would hear that someone had arrived in Athens to represent Persia in peace negotiations, and would then send representatives of their own without delay. So they did this on purpose, so that the Spartans might be present when they declared their views.

Accordingly, when Alexander had finished his speech, the Spartan envoys spoke in their turn: "The Spartans have sent us here to beg you not to endanger Greece by a departure from your previous policy, and to listen to no proposals from Persia. For any of the Greeks to do such a thing would be inconsistent with decency and honour; for you it would be far worse, for many reasons. It was you, in the first place, who started this war—our wishes were not considered. It began by being a war for your territories only—now all Greece is involved. Again, it would be an intolerable thing that the Athenians, who in the past have been known so often as liberators, should now be the cause of bringing slavery upon Greece. We do, however, sympathize with you in your hardships—the loss of two successive harvests and the ruin of your homes and property over so long a time; and in compensation we offer, in the name of Sparta and her allies, to provide support for all the women and other non-combatant members of your households, for as long as the war lasts.

"Do not let Alexander's smooth-sounding version of Mardonius' proposals seduce you; he does only what one might expect of him—a despot himself, of course he collaborates with a despot. But such conduct is not for you—at least, not if you are wise; for surely you know that in foreigners there is neither truth nor honour."

The Athenians then gave Alexander their answer. "We know," it ran, "as well as you do that the Persian strength is many times greater than our own: that, at least, is a fact which you need not rub in. Nevertheless, such is our love of freedom, that we will defend ourselves in whatever way we can. As for making terms with Persia, it is useless to persuade us; for we shall never consent. And now tell Mardonius, that so long as the sun keeps his present course in the sky, we Athenians will never make peace with Xerxes. On the contrary, we shall oppose him unremittingly, putting our trust in the help of the gods and heroes whom he despised, whose temples and statues he destroyed with fire. Never come to us again with a proposal like this, and never think you are doing us good service when you urge us to a course which is outrageous—for it would be a pity if you were the victim of an unfortunate incident in Athens, when you are our friend and benefactor."

So much for the Athenians' answer to Alexander. To the Spartan envoys they said: "No doubt it was natural that the Lacedaemonians should dread the possibility of our making terms with Persia; nonetheless it shows a poor estimate of the spirit of Athens. There is not so much gold in the world nor land so fair that we would take it for pay to join the common enemy and bring Greece into subjection. There are many compelling reasons against our doing so, even if we wished: the first and greatest is the burning of the temples and images of our gods—now ashes and rubble. It is our bounden duty to avenge this desecration with all our might—not to clasp the hand that wrought it. Again, there is the Greek nation—the community of blood and language, temples and ritual; our common way of life; if Athens were to betray all this, it would not be well done. We would have you know, therefore, if you did not know it already, that so long as a single Athenian remains alive we will make no peace with Xerxes. We are deeply moved, however, by your kindness and thoughtfulness, and the offer you made to provide for our families in this time of distress. Nothing could be more generous; nevertheless we prefer to carry on as best we can, without being a burden to you. That being our resolve, get your army into the field with the least possible delay; for unless we are much mistaken, it will not be long before the enemy invades Attica—he will do it the instant he gets the news that we refuse his requests. Now, therefore, before he can appear in Attica, it is time for us to meet him in Boeotia.''

Athens had given her answer; and the Spartan envoys left for home.

JOHN LOCKE was born the son of an attorney in Wrington, England, in 1632. Though he studied rhetoric, grammar, philosophy, geometry, and Greek at Oxford, Locke reserved his greatest interest for science and medicine, not then considered important academic subjects. He experimented with chemistry, meteorology, and medical science in collaboration with Robert Boyle and Thomas Sydenham. After earning his M.A. in 1658, Locke served as a tutor and fellow at Oxford, went on a diplomatic mission for two years, and in 1667 joined the household of Lord Ashley as a physician, meanwhile continuing his own research and writing projects. After Ashley was named 1st Lord Shaftesbury and made lord high chancellor of England in 1672, Locke served as Shaftesbury's secretary on the Council of Trade and Plantations. When political controversies shook Shaftesbury from favor in 1683, Locke had to flee England for Holland. He returned to England in 1689, enjoyed a degree of political influence, and saw his work through publication. Locke died in 1704.

A selection from *Of Civil Government: Second Treatise*. Publisher: Gateway Editions, Ltd., 1955. Portions of Chapters II, III, IV, V, VII, VIII, IX, and XI.

Of Civil Government

THE INTRODUCTION

He that will not give just occasion to think that all government in the world is the product only of force and violence, and that men live together by no other rules but that of beasts, where the strongest carries it, and so lay a foundation for perpetual disorder and mischief, tumult, sedition, and rebellion . . . must of necessity find out another rise of government, another original of political power. . . .

To this purpose, I think it may not be amiss to set down what I take to be political power; that the power of a magistrate over a subject may be distinguished from that of a father over his children, a master over his servant, a husband over his wife, and a lord over his slave.

Political power, then, I take to be a right of making laws with penalties of death, and consequently all less penalties, for the regulating and preserving of property, and of employing the force of the community in the execution of such laws, and in the defence of the commonwealth from foreign injury, and all this only for the public good.

OF THE STATE OF NATURE

To understand political power aright, and derive it from its original, we must consider what state all men are naturally in, and that is a state of perfect freedom to order their actions and dispose of their possessions and persons as they think fit, within the bounds of the law of nature, without asking leave, or depending upon the will of any other man.

A state also of equality, wherein all the power and jurisdiction is reciprocal, no one having more than another; there being nothing more evident than that creatures of the same species and rank, promiscuously born to all the same advantages of nature, and the use of the same faculties, should also be equal one amongst another without subordination or subjection. . . .

But though this be a state of liberty, yet it is not a state of licence; though man in that state has an uncontrollable liberty to dispose of his person or possessions, yet he has not liberty to destroy himself, or so much as any creature in his possession, but where some nobler use than its bare preservation calls for it. The state of nature has a law of nature to govern it, which obliges every one; and reason, which is that law, teaches all mankind who will but consult it, that, being all equal and independent, no one ought to harm another in his life, health, liberty, or possessions. For men being all the workmanship of one omnipotent and infinitely wise Maker—all the servants of one sovereign Master, sent into the world by His order, and about His business—they are His property, whose workmanship they are, made to last during His, not one another's pleasure; and being furnished with like faculties, sharing all in one community of nature, there cannot be supposed any such subordination among us, that may authorise us to destroy one another, as if we were made for one another's uses, as the inferior ranks of creatures are for ours. Every one, as he is bound to preserve himself, and not to quit his station wilfully, so, by the like reason, when his own preservation comes not in competition, ought he, as much as he can, to preserve the rest of mankind, and not, unless it be to do justice on an offender, take away or impair the life, or what tends to the preservation of the life, the liberty, health, limb, or goods of another.

And that all men may be restrained from invading others' rights, and from doing hurt to one another, and the law of nature be observed, which wills the peace and preservation of all mankind, the execution of the law of nature is in that state put into every man's hand, whereby every one has a right to punish the transgressors of that law to such a degree as may hinder its violation. For the law of nature would, as all other laws that concern men in this world, be in vain if there were nobody that, in the state of nature, had a power to execute that law, and thereby preserve the innocent and restrain offenders. And if any one in the state of nature may punish another for any evil he has done, every one may do so. For in that state of perfect equality, where naturally there is no superiority or jurisdiction of one over another, what any may do in prosecution of that law, every one must needs have a right to do.

And thus in the state of nature one man comes by a power over another; but yet no absolute or arbitrary power, to use a criminal, when he has got him in his hands, according to the passionate heats or boundless extravagance of his own will; but only to retribute to him so far as calm reason and conscience dictate what is proportionate to his transgression, which is so much as may serve for reparation and restraint. For these two are the only reasons why one man may lawfully do harm to another, which is that we call punishment. In transgressing the law of nature, the offender declares himself to live by another rule than that of common reason and equity, which is that measure God has set to the actions of men, for their mutual security; and so he becomes dangerous to mankind, the tie which is to secure them from injury and violence being slighted and broken by him. Which, being a trespass against the whole species, and the peace and safety of it, provided for by the law of nature, every man upon this score, by the right he hath to preserve mankind in general, may restrain, or, where it is necessary, destroy things noxious to them, and so may bring such evil on any one who has transgressed that law, as may make him repent the doing of it, and thereby deter him, and by his example others, from doing the like mischief. And in this case, and upon this ground, every man has a right to punish the offender, and be executioner of the law of nature.

To this strange doctrine—viz., That in the state of nature every one has the executive power of the law of nature—I doubt not but it will be objected that it is unreasonable for men to be judges in their own cases, that self-love will make men partial to themselves and their friends. And on the other side, that ill-nature, passion, and revenge will carry them too far in punishing others; and hence nothing but confusion and disorder will follow; and that therefore God has certainly appointed government to restrain the partiality and violence of men. I easily grant that civil government is the proper remedy for the inconveniences of the state of nature, which must certainly be great where men may be judges in their own case, since 'tis easy to be imagined that he who was so unjust as to do his brother an injury, will scarce be so just as to condemn himself for it. But I shall desire those who make this objection, to remember that absolute monarchs are but men, and if government is to be the remedy of those evils which necessarily follow from men's being judges in their own cases, and the state of nature is therefore not to be endured, I desire to know what kind of government that is, and how much better it is than the state of nature, where one man commanding a multitude, has the liberty to be judge in his own case, and may do to all his subjects whatever he pleases, without the least question or control of those who execute his pleasure; and in whatsoever he does, whether led by reason, mistake, or passion, must be submitted to, which men in the state of nature are not bound to do one to another? And if he that judges, judges amiss in his own or any other case, he is answerable for it to the rest of mankind.

'Tis often asked as a mighty objection, Where are, or ever were there, any men in such a state of nature? To which it may suffice as an answer at present: That since all princes and rulers of independent governments all through the world are in a state of nature, 'tis plain the world never was, nor ever will be, without numbers of men in that state. I have named all governors of independent communities, whether they are or are not in league with others. For 'tis not every compact that puts an end to the state of nature between men, but only this one of agreeing together mutually to enter into one community, and make one body politic; other promises and compacts men may make one with another, and yet still be in the state of nature. The promises and bargains for truck, etc., between the two men in Soldania, in or between a Swiss and an Indian, in the woods of America, are binding to them, though they are perfectly in a state of nature in reference to one another. For truth and keeping of faith belong to men as men, and not as members of society.

To those that say there were never any men in the state of nature. . . , I affirm that all men are naturally in that state, and remain so, till by their own consents they make themselves members of some politic society; and I doubt not, in the sequel of this discourse, to make it very clear.

OF THE STATE OF WAR

The state of war is a state of enmity and destruction; and therefore declaring by word or action, not a passionate and hasty, but a sedate, settled design upon another man's life, puts him in a state of war with him against whom he has declared such an intention, and so has exposed his life to the other's power to be taken away by him, or any one that joins with him in his defence and espouses his quarrel; it being reasonable and just I should have a right to destroy that which threatens me with destruction. For by the fundamental law of nature, man being to be preserved as much as possible, when all cannot be preserved, the safety of the innocent is to be preferred; and one may destroy a man who makes war upon him, or has discovered an enmity to his being, for the same reason that he may kill a wolf or a lion; because they are not under the ties of the common law of reason, have no other rule but that of force and violence, and so may be treated as a beast of prey, those dangerous and noxious creatures that will be sure to destroy him whenever he falls into their power.

And hence it is that he who attempts to get another man into his absolute power does thereby put himself into a state of war with him; it being to be understood as a declaration of a design upon his life. For I have reason to conclude that he who would get me into his power without my consent, would use me as he pleased when he had got me there, and destroy me too, when he had a fancy to it; for nobody can desire to have me in his absolute power, unless it be to compel me by force to that which is against the right of my freedom, i.e., make me a slave. To be free from such force is the only security of my preservation; and reason bids me look on him as an enemy to my preservation who would take away that freedom which is the fence to it; so that he who makes an attempt to enslave me, thereby puts himself into a state of war with me. He that in the state of nature would take away the freedom that belongs to any one in that state, must necessarily be supposed to have a design to take away everything else, that freedom being the foundation of all the rest; as he that in the state of society would take away the freedom belonging to those of that society or commonwealth, must be supposed to design to take away from them everything else, and so be looked on as in a state of war.

This makes it lawful for a man to kill a thief who has not in the least hurt him, nor declared any design upon his life, any farther than by the use of force so to get him in his power as to take away his money or what he pleases from him; because using force, where he has no right, to get me into his power, let his pretence be what it will, I have no reason to suppose that he who would take away my liberty would not, when he had me in his power, take away everything else. And therefore it is lawful for me to treat him as one who has put himself into a state of war with me, i.e., kill him, if I can; for to that hazard does he justly expose himself, whoever introduces a state of war and is aggressor in it.

And here we have the plain difference between the state of nature and the state of war, which however some men have confounded, are as far distant as a state of peace, good-will, mutual assistance and preservation, and a state of enmity, malice, violence and mutual destruction, are one from another. Men living together according to reason, without a common superior on earth with authority to judge between them, is properly the state of nature. But force, or a declared design of force, upon the person of another, where there is no common superior on earth to appeal to for relief, is the state of war; and 'tis the want of such an appeal gives a man the right of war even against an aggressor, though he be in society and a fellow-subject. Thus a thief, whom I cannot harm, but by appeal to the law, for having stolen all that I am worth, I may kill, when he sets on to rob me but of my horse or coat; because the law, which was made for my preservation where it cannot interpose to secure my life from present force, which if lost is capable of no reparation, permits me my own defence, and the right of war, a liberty to kill the aggressor, because the aggressor allows not time to appeal to our common judge, nor the decision of the law, for remedy in a case where the mischief may be irreparable. Want of a common judge with authority puts all men in a state of nature; force without right, upon a man's person, makes a state of war, both where is, and is not, a common judge.

But when the actual force is over, the state of war ceases between those that are in society, and are equally on both sides subject to the judge. . . .

OF SLAVERY

The natural liberty of man is to be free from any superior power on earth, and not to be under the will or legislative authority of man, but to have only the law of nature for his rule. The liberty of man in society is to be under no other legislative power but that established by consent in the commonwealth; nor under the dominion of any will or restraint of any law, but what that legislative shall enact according to the trust put in it. Freedom then is not . . . "a liberty for every one to do what he lists, to live as he pleases, and not to be tied by any laws." But freedom of men under government is to have a standing rule to live by, common to every one of that society, and made by the legislative power erected in it; a liberty to follow my own will in all things, where that rule prescribes not; and not to be subject to the inconstant, uncertain, unknown, arbitrary will of another man: as freedom of nature is to be under no other restraint but the law of nature.

This freedom from absolute arbitrary power is so necessary to, and closely joined with, a man's preservation, that he cannot part with it but by what forfeits his preservation and life together. For a man not having the power of his own life cannot by compact, or his own consent, enslave himself to any one, nor put himself under the absolute arbitrary power of another to take away his life when he pleases. Nobody can give more power than he has himself; and he that cannot take away his own life, cannot give another power over it. Indeed, having by his fault forfeited his own life by some act that deserves death, he to whom he has forfeited it may (when he has him in his power) delay to take it, and make use of him to his own service; and he does him no injury by it. For whenever he finds the hardship of his slavery outweighs the value of his life, 'tis in his power by resisting the will of his master to draw on himself the death he desires.

This is the perfect condition of slavery, which is nothing else but the state of war continued between a lawful conqueror and a captive. For if once compact enter between them, and make an agreement for a limited power on the one side, and obedience on the other, the state of war and slavery ceases as long as the compact endures. For, as has been said, no man can by agreement pass over to another that which he has not in himself, a power over his own life. . . .

OF PROPERTY

Whether we consider natural reason, which tells us that men being once born have a right to their preservation, and consequently to meat and drink and such other things as nature affords for their subsistence; or Revelation, which gives us an account of those grants God made of the world to Adam, and to Noah and his sons, 'tis very clear that God, as King David says, Psalm cxv. 16, "has given the earth to the children of men," given it to mankind in common. But this being supposed, it seems to some a very great difficulty how any one should ever come to have a property in anything. . . . I shall endeavour to show how men might come to have a property in several parts of that which God gave to mankind in common, and that without any express compact of all the commoners.

Though the earth and all inferior creatures be common to all men, yet every man has a property in his own person; this nobody has any right to but himself. The labour of his body and the work of his hands we may say are properly his. Whatsoever, then, he removes out of the state that nature has provided and left it in, he has mixed his labour with, and joined to it something that is his own, and thereby makes it his property. It being by him removed from the common state nature placed it in, it has by this labour something annexed to it that excludes the common right of other men. For this labour being the unquestionable property of the labourer, no man but he can have a right to what that is once joined to, at least where there is enough, and as good left in common for others.

He that is nourished by the acorns he picked up under an oak, or the apples he gathered from the trees in the wood, has certainly appropriated them to himself. Nobody can deny but the nourishment is his. I ask, then, When did they begin to be his—when he digested, or when he ate, or when he boiled, or when he brought them home, or when he picked them up? And 'tis plain if the first gathering made them not his, nothing else could. That labour put a distinction between them and common; that added something to them more than Nature, the common mother of all, had done, and so they became his private right. And will any one say he had no right to those acorns or apples he thus appropriated, because he had not the consent of all mankind to make them his? Was it a robbery thus to assume to himself what belonged to all in common? If such a consent as that was necessary, man had starved, notwithstanding the plenty God had given him. We see in commons which remain so by compact that 'tis the taking any part of what is common and removing it out of the state nature leaves it in, which begins the property; without which the common is of no use. And the taking of this or that part does not depend on the express consent of all the commoners. Thus the grass my horse has bit, the turfs my servant has cut, and the ore I have dug in any place where I have a right to them in common with others, become my property without the assignation or consent of anybody. The labour that was mine removing them out of that common state they were in, has fixed my property in them. . . .

It will perhaps be objected to this, that if gathering the acorns, or other fruits of the earth, etc., makes a right to them, then any one may engross as much as he will. To which I answer, Not so. The same law of nature that does by this means give us property, does also bound that property too. "God has given

us all things richly"(I Tim. vi. 17), is the voice of reason confirmed by inspiration. But how far has He given it to us? To
enjoy. As much as any one can make use of to any advantage
of life before it spoils, so much he may by his labour fix a
property in; whatever is beyond this, is more than his share,
and belongs to others. . . .

But the chief matter of property being now not the fruits of
the earth, and the beasts that subsist on it, but the earth itself,
as that which takes in and carries with it all the rest, I think
it is plain that property in that, too, is acquired as the former.
As much land as a man tills, plants, improves, cultivates, and
can use the product of, so much is his property. He by his
labour does as it were enclose it from the common. Nor will it
invalidate his right to say, everybody else has an equal title to
it; and therefore he cannot appropriate, he cannot enclose, without the consent of all his fellow-commoners, all mankind. God,
when He gave the world in common to all mankind, commanded man also to labour, and the penury of his condition
required it of him. God and his reason commanded him to
subdue the earth, i.e., improve it for the benefit of life, and
therein lay out something upon it that was his own, his labour.
He that, in obedience to this command of God, subdued, tilled,
and sowed any part of it, thereby annexed to it something that
was his property, which another had no title to, nor could without injury take from him.

Nor was this appropriation of any parcel of land, by improving it, any prejudice to any other man, since there was still
enough and as good left; and more than the yet unprovided
could use. So that in effect there was never the less left for others
because of his enclosure for himself. For he that leaves as much
as another can make use of, does as good as take nothing at all.
Nobody could think himself injured by the drinking of another
man, though he took a good draught, who had a whole river
of the same water left him to quench his thirst; and the case

of land and water, where there is enough of both, is perfectly the same. . . .

This is certain, that in the beginning, before the desire of having more than man needed had altered the intrinsic value of things, which depends only on their usefulness to the life of man; or had agreed that a little piece of yellow metal which would keep without wasting or decay should be worth a great piece of flesh or a whole heap of corn, though men had a right to appropriate by their labour, each one to himself, as much of the things of nature as he could use, yet this could not be much, nor to the prejudice of others, where the same plenty was still left to those who would use the same industry.

Before the appropriation of land, he who gathered as much of the wild fruit, killed, caught, or tamed as many of the beasts as he could; he that so employed his pains about any of the spontaneous products of nature as any way to alter them from the state which nature put them in, by placing any of his labour on them, did thereby acquire a propriety in them. But if they perished in his possession without their due use; if the fruits rotted, or the venison putrified before he could spend it, he offended against the common law of nature, and was liable to be punished; he invaded his neighbour's share, for he had no right further than his use called for any of them and they might serve to afford him conveniences of life.

The same measures governed the possessions of land, too. Whatsoever he tilled and reaped, laid up, and made use of before it spoiled, that was his peculiar right; whatsoever he enclosed and could feed and make use of, the cattle and product was also his. But if either the grass of his enclosure rotted on the ground, or the fruit of his planting perished without gathering and laying up, this part of the earth, notwithstanding his enclosure, was still to be looked on as waste, and might be the possession of any other. Thus, at the beginning, Cain might take as much ground as he could till and make it his own land,

and yet leave enough for Abel's sheep to feed on; a few acres would serve for both their possessions. But as families increased, and industry enlarged their stocks, their possessions enlarged with the need of them; but yet it was commonly without any fixed property in the ground they made use of, till they incorporated, settled themselves together, and built cities; and then, by consent, they came in time to set out the bounds of their distinct territories, and agree on limits between them and their neighbours, and, by laws within themselves, settled the properties of those of the same society. For we see that in that part of the world which was first inhabited, and therefore like to be the best peopled, even as low down as Abraham's time they wandered with their flocks and their herds, which were their substance, freely up and down; and this Abraham did in a country where he was a stranger: whence it is plain that at least a great part of the land lay in common; that the inhabitants valued it not, nor claimed property in any more than they made use of. But when there was not room enough in the same place for their herds to feed together, they by consent . . . separated and enlarged their pasture where it best liked them. . . .

Nor is it so strange, as perhaps before consideration it may appear, that the property of labour should be able to overbalance the community of land. For it is labour indeed that puts the difference of value on everything; and let any one consider what the difference is between an acre of land planted with tobacco or sugar, sown with wheat or barley, and an acre of the same land lying in common without any husbandry upon it, and he will find that the improvement of labour makes the far greater part of the value. I think it will be but a very modest computation to say that of the products of the earth useful to the life of man nine-tenths are the effects of labour; nay, if we will rightly estimate things as they come to our use, and cast up the several expenses about them — what in them is purely owing to nature, and what to labour — we shall find that in most of them ninety-nine hundredths are wholly to be put on the account of labour. . . .

To make this a little clearer, let us but trace some of the ordinary provisions of life through their several progresses before they come to our use, and see how much they receive of their value from human industry. Bread, wine, and cloth are things of daily use and great plenty; yet, notwithstanding, acorns, water, and leaves or skins, must be our bread, drink, and clothing, did not labour furnish us with these more useful commodities. For whatever bread is more worth than acorns, wine than water, and cloth or silk than leaves, skins, or moss, that is wholly owing to labour and industry: the one of these being the food and raiment which unassisted nature furnishes us with; the other, provisions which our industry and pains prepare for us; which how much they exceed the other in value when any one has computed, he will then see how much labour makes the far greatest part of the value of things we enjoy in this world. And the ground which produces the materials is scarce to be reckoned in as any, or at most but a very small, part of it; so little that even amongst us land that is left wholly to nature, that has no improvement of pasturage, tillage, or planting, is called, as indeed it is, "waste," and we shall find the benefit of it amount to little more than nothing. . . .

From all which it is evident that, though the things of nature are given in common, yet man, by being master of himself and proprietor of his own person and the actions or labour of it, had still in himself the great foundation of property; and that which made up the great part of what he applied to the support or comfort of his being, when invention and arts had improved the conveniences of life, was perfectly his own, and did not belong in common to others.

Thus labour, in the beginning, gave a right of property, wherever any one was pleased to employ it upon what was common, which remained a long while the far greater part, and is yet more than mankind makes use of. Men at first, for the most part, contented themselves with what unassisted nature offered to their necessities; and though afterwards, in some parts of the world (where the increase of people and stock, with the use of money, had made land scarce, and so of some value), the several communities settled the bounds of their distinct territories, and, by laws within themselves, regulated the properties of the private men of their society, and so, by compact and agreement, settled the property which labour and industry began—and the leagues that have been made between several states and kingdoms, either expressly or tacitly disowning all claim and right to the land in the other's possession, have, by common consent, given up their pretences to their natural common right, which originally they had to those countries; and so have, by positive agreement, settled a property amongst themselves in distinct parts of the world—yet there are still great tracts of ground to be found which, the inhabitants thereof not having joined with the rest of mankind in the consent of the use of their common money, lie waste, and are more than the people who dwell on it do or can make use of, and so still lie in common; though this can scarce happen amongst that part of mankind that have consented to the use of money.

The greatest part of things really useful to the life of man, and such as the necessity of subsisting made the first commoners of the world look after, as it does the Americans now, are generally things of short duration, such as, if they are not consumed by use, will decay and perish of themselves: gold, silver, and diamonds are things that fancy or agreement have put the value on more than real use and the necessary support of life. Now, of those good things which nature has provided in common, every one had a right, as has been said, to as much as he could use, and had a property in all he could effect with his labour—all that his industry could extend to, to alter from the state nature had put it in, was his. He that gathered a hundred bushels of acorns or apples had thereby a property in them; they were his goods as soon as gathered. He was only to look that he used them before they spoiled, else he took more than his share, and robbed others; and, indeed, it was a foolish thing, as well as dishonest, to hoard up more than he could make use of. If he gave away a part to anybody else, so that it perished not uselessly in his possession, these he also made use of; and if he also bartered away plums that would have rotted in a week, for nuts that would last good for his eating a whole year, he did no injury; he wasted not the common stock, destroyed no part of the portion of goods that belonged to others, so long as nothing perished uselessly in his hands. Again, if he would give his nuts for a piece of metal, pleased with its colour, or exchange his sheep for shells, or wool for a sparkling pebble or a diamond, and keep those by him all his life, he invaded not the right of others; he might heap up as much of these durable things as he pleased, the exceeding of the bounds of his just property not lying in the largeness of his possessions, but the perishing of anything uselessly in it.

And thus came in the use of money—some lasting thing that men might keep without spoiling, and that, by mutual consent, men would take in exchange for the truly useful but perishable supports of life.

And as different degrees of industry were apt to give men possessions in different proportions, so this invention of money gave them the opportunity to continue and enlarge them; for supposing an island, separate from all possible commerce with the rest of the world, wherein there were but a hundred families—but there were sheep, horses, and cows, with other useful animals, wholesome fruits, and land enough for corn for a hundred thousand times as many, but nothing in the island, either because of its commonness or perishableness, fit to supply the place of money—what reason could any one have there to enlarge his possessions beyond the use of his family and a plentiful supply to its consumption, either in what their own industry produced, or they could barter for like perishable useful commodities with others? Where there is not something both lasting and scarce, and so valuable to be hoarded up, there men will not be apt to enlarge their possessions of land, were it never so rich, never so free for them to take; for I ask, what would a man value ten thousand or a hundred thousand acres of excellent land, ready cultivated, and well stocked too with cattle, in the middle of the inland parts of America, where he had no hopes of commerce with other parts of the world, to draw money to him by the sale of the product? It would not be worth the enclosing, and we should see him give up again to the wild common of nature whatever was more than would supply the conveniences of life to be had there for him and his family. . . .

Since gold and silver, being little useful to the life of man in proportion to food, raiment, and carriage, has its value only from the consent of men, whereof labour yet makes, in great part, the measure, it is plain that the consent of men have agreed to a disproportionate and unequal possession of the earth—I mean out of the bounds of society and compact; for in governments the laws regulate it; they having, by consent, found out and agreed in a way how a man may rightfully and without injury possess more than he himself can make use of by receiving gold and silver, which may continue long in a man's possession, without decaying for the overplus, and agreeing those metals should have a value.

And thus, I think, it is very easy to conceive without any difficulty how labour could at first begin a title of property in the common things of nature, and how the spending it upon our uses bounded it; so that there could then be no reason of quarrelling about title, nor any doubt about the largeness of possession it gave. Right and conveniency went together; for as a man had a right to all he could employ his labour upon, so he had no temptation to labour for more than he could make use of. This left no room for controversy about the title, nor for encroachment on the right of others; what portion a man carved to himself was easily seen, and it was useless, as well as dishonest, to carve himself too much, or take more than he needed.

*   *   *

OF POLITICAL OR CIVIL SOCIETY

God having made man such a creature, that in his own judgment it was not good for him to be alone, put him under strong obligations of necessity, convenience, and inclination to drive him into society, as well as fitted him with understanding and language to continue and enjoy it. The first society was between man and wife, which gave beginning to that between parents and children; to which, in time, that between master and servant came to be added; and though all these might, and commonly did meet together, and make up but one family, wherein the master or mistress of it had some sort of rule proper to a family; each of these, or all together, came short of political society, as we shall see, if we consider the different ends, ties, and bounds of each of these. . . .

Let us therefore consider a master of a family, with all these subordinate relations of wife, children, servants, and slaves, united under the domestic rule of a family, which, what resemblance soever it may have in its order, offices, and number too, with a little commonwealth, yet is very far from it both in its constitution, power and end; or, if it must be thought a monarchy, and the paterfamilias the absolute monarch in it, absolute monarchy will have but a very shattered and short power, when 'tis plain, by what has been said before, that the master of the family has a very distinct and differently limited power, both as to time and extent, over those several persons that are in it; for, excepting slaves (and the family is as much a family, and his power as paterfamilias as great, whether there be any slaves in the family or no), he has no legislative power of life and death over any of them, and none, too, but what a mistress of a family may have as well as he. And he certainly can have no absolute power over the whole family, who has but a very limited one over every individual in it. But how a family or any other society of men differ from that, which is properly political society, we shall best see by considering wherein political society itself consists.

Man being born, as has been proved, with a title to perfect freedom, and an uncontrolled enjoyment of all the rights and privileges of the law of nature equally with any other man or number of men in the world, has by nature a power not only to preserve his property—that is, his life, liberty, and estate—against the injuries and attempts of other men, but to judge of and punish the breaches of that law in others as he is persuaded the offence deserves, even with death itself, in crimes where the heinousness of the fact in his opinion requires it. But because no political society can be nor subsist without having in itself the power to preserve the property, and, in order thereunto, punish the offences of all those of that society, there, and there only, is political society, where every one of the members has quitted this natural power, resigned it up into the hands of the community in all cases that exclude him not from appealing for protection to the law established by it; and thus all private judgment of every particular member being excluded, the community comes to be umpire, by settled standing rules; indifferent, and the same to all parties. And by men authorized by the community for their execution, [it] decides all the differences that may happen between any members of that society concerning any matter of right, and punishes those offences which any member has committed against the society with such penalties as the law has established; whereby it is easy to discern who are and who are not in political society together. Those

who are united into one body, and have a common established
law and judicature to appeal to, with authority to decide controversies between them and punish offenders, are in civil society
one with another; but those who have no such common
appeal—I mean on earth—are still in the state of nature, each
being, where there is no other, judge for himself and executioner,
which is, as I have before shown it, the perfect state of nature. . . .

Hence it is evident that absolute monarchy, which by some
men is counted the only government in the world, is indeed
inconsistent with civil society, and so can be no form of civil
government at all. For the end of civil society being to avoid
and remedy those inconveniences of the state of nature which
necessarily follow from every man's being judge in his own case,
by setting up a known authority to which every one of that
society may appeal upon any injury received or controversy that
may arise, and which every one of the society ought to obey;
wherever any persons are who have not such an authority to
appeal to and decide any difference between them there, those
persons are still in the state of nature. And so is every absolute
prince, in respect of those who are under his dominion. . . .

OF THE BEGINNING OF POLITICAL SOCIETIES

Men being, as has been said, by nature all free, equal, and
independent, no one can be put out of this estate, and subjected
to the political power of another, without his own consent, which
is done by agreeing with other men to join and unite into a
community for their comfortable, safe, and peaceable living one
amongst another, in a secure enjoyment of their properties, and
a greater security against any that are not of it. This any number
of men may do, because it injures not the freedom of the rest;
they are left as they were in the liberty of the state of nature.
When any number of men have so consented to make one
community or government, they are thereby presently incor-

porated, and make one body politic, wherein the majority have a right to act and conclude the rest.

For when any number of men have, by the consent of every individual, made a community, they have thereby made that community one body, with a power to act as one body, which is only by the will and determination of the majority. For that which acts any community being only the consent of the individuals of it, and it being one body must move one way, it is necessary the body should move that way whither the greater force carries it, which is the consent of the majority; or else it is impossible it should act or continue one body, one community, which the consent of every individual that united into it agreed that it should; and so every one is bound by that consent to be concluded by the majority. And therefore we see that in assemblies empowered to act by positive laws, where no number is set by that positive law which empowers them, the act of the majority passes for the act of the whole, and of course determines, as having by the law of nature and reason the power of the whole.

And thus every man, by consenting with others to make one body politic under one government, puts himself under an obligation to every one of that society, to submit to the determination of the majority, and to be concluded by it; or else this original compact, whereby he with others incorporates into one society, would signify nothing, and be no compact, if he be left free and under no other ties than he was in before in the state of nature. For what appearance would there be of any compact? What new engagement if he were no farther tied by any decrees of the society, than he himself thought fit, and did actually consent to? This would be still as great a liberty as he himself had before his compact, or any one else in the state of nature has, who may submit himself and consent to any acts of it if he thinks fit.

For if the consent of the majority shall not in reason be received as the act of the whole and conclude every individual,

nothing but the consent of every individual can make anything
to be the act of the whole, which considering the infirmities of
health and avocations of business, which in a number, though
much less than that of a commonwealth, will necessarily keep
many away from the public assembly, and the variety of opinions, and contrariety of interest, which unavoidably happen in
all collections of men, 'tis next to impossible ever to be had.
And therefore if the coming into society be upon such terms it
will be only like Cato's coming into the theatre, *tantum ut exiret*.
Such a constitution as this would make the mighty leviathan
of a shorter duration than the feeblest creatures, and not let it
outlast the day it was born in; which cannot be supposed till
we can think that rational creatures should desire and constitute
societies only to be dissolved. For where the majority cannot
conclude the rest, there they cannot act as one body, and consequently will be immediately dissolved again.

Whosoever therefore out of a state of nature unite into a
community must be understood to give up all the power necessary to the ends for which they unite into society, to the
majority of the community, unless they expressly agreed in any
number greater than the majority. And this is done by barely
agreeing to unite into one political society, which is all the
compact that is, or needs be, between the individuals that enter
into or make up a commonwealth. And thus that which begins
and actually constitutes any political society is nothing but the
consent of any number of freemen capable of a majority to unite
and incorporate into such a society. And this is that, and that
only, which did or could give beginning to any lawful government in the world.

*   *   *

OF THE ENDS OF POLITICAL SOCIETY AND GOVERNMENT

If man in the state of nature be so free, as has been said, if he be absolute lord of his own person and possessions, equal to the greatest, and subject to nobody, why will he part with his freedom, this empire, and subject himself to the dominion and control of any other power? To which, it is obvious to answer, that though in the state of nature he has such a right, yet the enjoyment of it is very uncertain, and constantly exposed to the invasions of others. For all being kings as much as he, every man his equal, and the greater part no strict observers of equity and justice, the enjoyment of the property he has in this state is very unsafe, very unsecure. This makes him willing to quit this condition, which, however free, is full of fears and continual dangers; and it is not without reason that he seeks out and is willing to join in society with others, who are already united, or have a mind to unite, for the mutual preservation of their lives, liberties, and estates, which I call by the general name, property.

The great and chief end, therefore, of men's uniting into commonwealths, and putting themselves under government, is the preservation of their property; to which in the state of nature there are many things wanting.

First, there wants an established, settled, known law, received and allowed by common consent to be the standard of right and wrong, and the common measure to decide all controversies between them. For though the law of nature be plain and intelligible to all rational creatures; yet men, being biased by their interest, as well as ignorant for want of study of it, are not apt to allow of it as a law binding to them in the application of it to their particular cases.

Secondly, in the state of nature there wants a known and indifferent judge, with authority to determine all differences according to the established law. For every one in that state, being both judge and executioner of the law of nature, men being partial to themselves, passion and revenge is very apt to carry them too far, and with too much heat in their own cases, as well as negligence and unconcernedness, to make them too remiss in other men's.

Thirdly, in the state of nature there often wants power to back and support the sentence when right, and to give it due execution. They who by any injustice offend, will seldom fail, where they are able by force to make good their injustice; such resistance many times makes the punishment dangerous, and frequently destructive to those who attempt it.

Thus mankind, notwithstanding all the privileges of the state of nature, being but in an ill condition, while they remain in it, are quickly driven into society. Hence it comes to pass that we seldom find any number of men live any time together in this state. The inconveniences that they are therein exposed to by the irregular and uncertain exercise of the power every man has of punishing the transgressions of others, make them take sanctuary under the established laws of government, and therein seek the preservation of their property. It is this makes them so willingly give up every one his single power of punishing, to be exercised by such alone, as shall be appointed to it amongst them; and by such rules as the community, or those authorised by them to that purpose, shall agree on. And in this we have the original right and rise of both the legislative and executive power, as well as of the governments and societies themselves.

For in the state of nature, to omit the liberty he has of innocent delights, a man has two powers.

The first is to do whatsoever he thinks fit for the preservation of himself, and others within the permission of the law of nature, by which law, common to them all, he and all the rest of mankind are of one community, make up one society, distinct from all other creatures. And were it not for the corruption and viciousness of degenerate men there would be no need of any other, no necessity that men should separate from this great and natural community, and associate into lesser combinations. The other power a man has in the state of nature is the power to punish the crimes committed against that law. Both these he gives up when he joins in a private, if I may so call it, or particular political society, and incorporates into any commonwealth separate from the rest of mankind.

The first power, viz., of doing whatsoever he thought fit for the preservation of himself and the rest of mankind, he gives up to be regulated by laws made by the society, so far forth as the preservation of himself and the rest of that society shall require; which laws of the society in many things confine the liberty he had by the law of nature.

Secondly, the power of punishing he wholly gives up, and engages his natural force (which he might before employ in the execution of the law of nature, by his own single authority as he thought fit), to assist the executive power of the society, as the law thereof shall require. For being now in a new state, wherein he is to enjoy many conveniences, from the labour, assistance, and society of others in the same community, as well as protection from its whole strength; he has to part also with as much of his natural liberty, in providing for himself, as the good, prosperity and safety of the society shall require; which is not only necessary but just, since the other members of the society do the like.

But though men when they enter into society give up the equality, liberty, and executive power they had in the state of nature into the hands of the society, to be so far disposed of by the legislative as the good of the society shall require; yet it being only with an intention in every one the better to preserve himself, his liberty and property (for no rational creature can be supposed to change his condition with an intention to be worse), the power of the society, or legislative constituted by them, can never be supposed to extend farther than the common good, but is obliged to secure every one's property by providing against those three defects above-mentioned that made the state of nature so unsafe and uneasy. And so whoever has the legislative or supreme power of any commonwealth is bound to govern by established standing laws, promulgated and known to the people, and not by extemporary decrees; by indifferent and upright judges, who are to decide controversies by those laws; and to employ the force of the community at home only in the execution of such laws, or abroad, to prevent or redress foreign injuries, and secure the community from inroads and invasion. And all this to be directed to no other end but the peace, safety, and public good of the people.

*   *   *

Of the Extent of the Legislative Power

The great end of men's entering into society being the enjoyment of their properties in peace and safety, and the great instrument and means of that being the laws established in that society: the first and fundamental positive law of all commonwealths, is the establishing of the legislative power; as the first and fundamental natural law, which is to govern even the legislative itself, is the preservation of the society, and (as far as will consist with the public good) of every person in it. This legislative is not only the supreme power of the commonwealth, but sacred and unalterable in the hands where the community have once placed it; nor can any edict of anybody else, in what form soever conceived, or by what power soever backed, have the force and obligation of a law, which has not its sanction from that legislative which the public has chosen and appointed. For without this the law could not have that, which is absolutely necessary to its being a law, the consent of the society over whom nobody can have a power to make laws; but by their own consent, and by authority received from them; and therefore all the obedience, which by the most solemn ties any one can be obliged to pay, ultimately terminates in this supreme power, and is directed by those laws which it enacts. . . .

Though the legislative, whether placed in one or more, whether it be always in being, or only by intervals, though it be the supreme power in every commonwealth, yet, first, it is not nor can possibly be absolutely arbitrary over the lives and fortunes of the people. For it being but the joint power of every member of the society given up to that person, or assembly, which is legislator; it can be no more than those persons had in a state of nature before they entered into society, and gave it up to the community. For nobody can transfer to another more power than he has in himself; and nobody has an absolute arbitrary power over himself, or over any other to destroy his own life, or take away the life or property of another. A man as has been proved cannot subject himself to the arbitrary power of another; and having in the state of nature no arbitrary power over the life, liberty, or possession of another, but only so much as the law of nature gave him for the preservation of himself, and the rest of mankind; this is all he does, or can give up to the commonwealth, and by it to the legislative power, so that the legislative can have no more than this. Their power in the utmost bounds of it, is limited to the public good of the society. It is a power that has no other end but preservation, and therefore can never have a right to destroy, enslave, or designedly to impoverish the subjects. The obligations of the law of nature cease not in society, but only in many cases are drawn closer, and have by human laws known penalties annexed to them to enforce their observation. Thus the law of nature stands as an eternal rule to all men, legislators as well as others. The rules that they make for other men's actions must, as well as their own, and other men's actions be conformable to the law of nature, i.e., to the will of God, of which that is a declaration, and the fundamental law of nature being the preservation of mankind, no human sanction can be good or valid against it.

Secondly, the legislative, or supreme authority, cannot assume to itself a power to rule by extemporary arbitrary decrees, but is bound to dispense justice, and decide the rights of the subject by promulgated standing laws, and known authorised judges. For the law of nature being unwritten, and so nowhere to be found but in the minds of men, they who through passion or interest shall miscite or misapply it, cannot so easily be convinced of their mistake where there is no established judge. And so it serves not, as it ought, to determine the rights, and fence the properties of those that live under it, especially where every one is judge, interpreter, and executioner of it too, and that in his own case; and he that has right on his side, having ordinarily but his own single strength has not force enough to defend himself from injuries, or punish delinquents. To avoid these inconveniences, which disorder men's properties in the state of nature, men unite into societies that they may have the united strength of the whole society to secure and defend their properties, and may have standing rules to bound it, by which every one may know what is his. To this end it is that men give up all their natural power to the society which they enter into, and the community put the legislative power into such hands as they think fit, with this trust, that they shall be governed by declared laws, or else their peace, quiet, and property, will still be at the same uncertainty as it was in the state of nature. . . .

Thirdly, the supreme power cannot take from any man any part of his property without his own consent. For the preservation of property being the end of government, and that for which men enter into society, it necessarily supposes and requires that the people should have property, without which they must be supposed to lose that by entering into society, which was the end for which they entered into it, too gross an absurdity for any man to own. Men, therefore, in society having property, they have such a right to the goods which by the law of the community are theirs, that nobody has a right to take them or any part of them from them, without their own consent; without this they have no property at all. For I have truly no property in that which another can by right take from me when he pleases, against my consent. Hence it is a mistake to think that the supreme or legislative power of any commonwealth can do what it will, and dispose of the estates of the subjects arbitrarily, or take any part of them at pleasure. This is not much to be feared in governments where the legislative consists wholly, or in part, in assemblies which are variable, whose members, upon the dissolution of the assembly, are subjects under the common laws of their country, equally with the rest. But in governments where the legislative is in one lasting assembly, always in being, or in one man, as in absolute monarchies, there is danger still, that they will think themselves to have a distinct interest from the rest of the community, and so will be apt to increase their own riches and power by taking what they think fit from the people. For a man's property is not at all secure, though there be good and equitable laws to set the bounds of it between him and his fellow subjects, if he who commands those subjects have power to take from any private man what part he pleases of his property, and use and dispose of it as he thinks good.

Fourthly, the legislative cannot transfer the power of making laws to any other hands; for it being but a delegated power from the people, they who have it cannot pass it over to others. The people alone can appoint the form of the commonwealth, which is by constituting the legislative, and appointing in whose hands that shall be. And when the people have said we will submit to rules, and be governed by laws made by such men, and in such forms, nobody else can say other men shall make laws for them; nor can the people be bound by any laws but such as are enacted by those whom they have chosen and authorised to make laws for them.

These are the bounds which the trust that is put in them by the society, and the law of God and Nature, have set to the legislative power of every commonwealth, in all forms of government.

First, they are to govern by promulgated established laws, not to be varied in particular cases, but to have one rule for rich and poor, for the favourite at court and the countryman at plough.

Secondly, these laws also ought to be designed for no other end ultimately but the good of the people.

Thirdly, they must not raise taxes on the property of the people without the consent of the people, given by themselves or their deputies. And this properly concerns only such governments where the legislative is always in being, or at least where the people have not reserved any part of the legislative to deputies, to be from time to time chosen by themselves.

Fourthly, the legislative neither must nor can transfer the power of making laws to anybody else, or place it anywhere but where the people have.

JONATHAN SWIFT was born in 1667 in Dublin, Ireland, to English parents. Swift's father died a few months before his birth, and he was raised by his mother and uncles. They sent him to an excellent Irish preparatory school and to Trinity College, Dublin, where he earned his B.A. in 1686. In 1689 Swift left Ireland for England and became secretary to Sir William Temple, a former diplomat and "man of culture." Swift aided Temple with the writing of essays and memoirs and read widely in Temple's personal library. Swift also discovered his gifts as a satirical writer at this time, and he wrote poetry. In 1692 he received an M.A. from Oxford. After Temple's death in 1699, Swift returned to Ireland and served in the Irish church hierarchy, but visited England frequently. He became a highly respected political pamphleteer in both Ireland and England, and his appointment as dean of St. Patrick's Cathedral in Dublin in 1713 was made as a political favor for his writing on the behalf of England's Tories. Swift's *A Tale of a Tub* was published in 1704 and *Gulliver's Travels* in 1726. Swift continued to work and write until a few years before his death in 1745.

From *Gulliver's Travels*. Editions of this work have been published by W. W. Norton & Co., Inc., Oxford University Press, Penguin Books, Random House, Inc., and other publishers.

Gulliver's Travels

BOOK IV

A Voyage to the Country of the Houyhnhnms

CHAPTER I

I continued at home with my wife and children about five months in a very happy condition, if I could have learned the lesson of knowing when I was well. I left my poor wife big with child, and accepted an advantageous offer made me to be Captain of the *Adventure,* a stout merchantman of 350 tons: for I understood navigation well, and being grown weary of a surgeon's employment at sea, which however I could exercise upon occasion, I took a skilful young man of that calling, one Robert Purefoy, into my ship. We set sail from Portsmouth upon the seventh day of August, 1710; on the fourteenth we met with Captain Pocock of Bristol, at Teneriffe, who was going to the bay of Campechy, to cut logwood. On the sixteenth he was parted from us by a storm; I heard since my return that his ship foundered, and none escaped but one cabin boy. He was an honest man, and a good sailor, but a little too positive in his own opinions, which was the cause of his destruction, as it hath been of several others. For if he had followed my advice, he might have been safe at home with his family at this time, as well as myself.

I had several men died in my ship of calentures, so that I was forced to get recruits out of Bardadoes, and the Leeward

Island, where I touched by the direction of the merchants who employed me, which I had soon too much cause to repent: for I found afterwards that most of them had been buccaneers. I had fifty hands on board, and my orders were that I should trade with the Indians in the South Sea, and make what discoveries I could. These rogues whom I had picked up debauched my other men, and they all formed a conspiracy to seize the ship and secure me; which they did one morning, rushing into my cabin, and binding me hand and foot, threatening to throw me overboard, if I offered to stir. I told them I was their prisoner and would submit. This they made me swear to do, and then they unbound me, only fastening one of my legs with a chain near my bed, and placed a sentry at my door with his piece charged, who was commanded to shoot me dead, if I attempted my liberty. They sent me down victuals and drink, and took the government of the ship to themselves. Their design was to turn pirates, and plunder the Spaniards, which they could not do, till they got more men. But first they resolved to sell the goods in the ship, and then go to Madagascar for recruits, several among them having died since my confinement. They sailed many weeks, and traded with the Indians, but I knew not what course they took, being kept a close prisoner in my cabin, and expecting nothing less than to be murdered, as they often threatened me.

Upon the ninth day of May, 1711, one James Welch came down to my cabin; and said he had orders from the Captain to set me ashore. I expostulated with him but in vain; neither would he so much as tell me who their new Captain was. They forced me into the long-boat, letting me put on my best suit of clothes, which were as good as new, and a small bundle of linen, but no arms except my hanger; and they were so civil as not to search my pockets, into which I conveyed what money I had, with some other little necessaries. They rowed about a league, and then set me down on a strand. I desired them to tell me what country it was. They swore they knew no more than myself, but said that the Captain (as they called him) was resolved, after they had sold the lading, to get rid of me in the first place where they could discover land. They pushed off immediately, advising me to make haste, for fear of being overtaken by the tide, and so bade me farewell.

In this desolate condition I advanced forward, and soon got upon firm ground, where I sat down on a bank to rest myself, and consider what I had best to do. When I was a little refreshed I went up into the country, resolving to deliver myself to the first savages I should meet, and purchase my life from them by some bracelets, glass rings, and other toys which sailors usually provide themselves with in those voyages, and whereof I had some about me. The land was divided by long rows of trees, not regularly planted, but naturally growing; there was plenty of grass, and several fields of oats. I walked very circumspectly for fear of being surprised, or suddenly shot with an arrow from behind or on either side. I fell into a beaten road, where I saw many tracks of human feet, and some of cows, but most of horses. At last I beheld several animals in a field, and one or two of the same kind sitting in trees. Their shape was very singular and deformed, which a little discomposed me, so that I lay down behind a thicket to observe them better. Some of them coming forward near the place where I lay, gave me an opportunity of distinctly marking their form. Their heads and breasts were covered with a thick hair, some frizzled and others lank; they had beards like goats, and a long ridge of hair down their backs and the fore-parts of their legs and feet, but the rest of their bodies were bare, so that I might see their skins, which were of a brown buff colour. They had no tails, nor any hair at all on their buttocks, except about the anus; which, I presume, nature had placed there to defend them as they sat on the ground; for this posture they used, as well as lying down, and often stood on their hind feet. They climbed high trees, as nimbly as a squirrel, for they had strong extended claws before and behind, terminating in sharp points, and hooked. They would often spring and bound and leap with prodigious agility. The females were not so large as the males; they had long lank hair on their heads, but none on their faces, nor any thing more than a sort of down on the rest of their bodies, except about the anus, and pudenda. Their dugs hung between their fore-feet, and often reached almost to the ground as they walked. The hair of both sexes was of several colours, brown, red, black, and yellow. Upon the whole, I never beheld in all my travels so disagreeable an animal, nor one against which I naturally conceived so strong an antipathy. So that thinking I had seen enough, full of contempt and aversion, I got up and pursued the beaten road, hoping it might direct me to the cabin of some Indian. I had not got far when I met one of these creatures full in my way, and coming up directly to me. The ugly monster, when he saw me, distorted several ways every feature of his visage, and stared as at an object he had never seen before; then approaching nearer, lifted up his fore-paw, whether out of curiosity or mischief, I could not tell. But I drew my hanger, and gave him a good blow with the flat side of it, for I durst not strike him with the edge, fearing the inhabitants might be provoked against me, if they should come to know that I had killed or maimed any of their cattle. When the beast felt the smart, he drew back, and roared so loud that a herd of at least forty came flocking about me from the next field, howling and making odious faces; but I ran to the body of a tree, and leaning my back against it, kept them off by waving my hanger. Several of this cursed brood, getting hold of the branches behind, leapt up into the tree, from whence they began to discharge their excrements on my head; however, I escaped pretty well, by sticking close to the stem of the tree, but was almost stifled with the filth, which fell about me on every side.

In the midst of this distress, I observed them all to run away on a sudden as fast as they could, at which I ventured to leave the tree, and pursue the road, wondering what it was that could put them into this fright. But looking on my left, I saw a horse walking softly in the field; which my persecutors having sooner discovered, was the cause of their flight. The horse started a little when he came near me, but soon recovering himself, looked full in my face with manifest tokens of wonder; he viewed my hands and feet, walking round me several times. I would have pursued my journey, but he placed himself directly in the way, yet looking with a very mild aspect, never offering the least violence. We stood gazing at each other for some time; at last I took the boldness to reach my hand towards his neck, with a design to stroke it, using the common style and whistle of jockeys when they are going to handle a strange horse. But this animal, seeming to receive my civilities with disdain, shook his head, and bent his brows, softly raising up his right fore-foot to remove my hand. Then he neighed three or four times, but in so different a cadence, that I almost began to think he was speaking to himself in some language of his own.

While he and I were thus employed, another horse came up: who applying himself to the first in a very formal manner, they gently struck each other's right hoof before, neighing several times by turns, and varying the sound, which seemed to be almost articulate. They went some paces off, as if it were to confer together, walking side by side, backward and forward, like persons deliberating upon some affair of weight, but often turning their eyes towards me, as it were to watch that I might not escape. I was amazed to see such actions and behaviour in brute beasts, and concluded with myself, that if the inhabitants of this country were endued with a proportionable degree of reason, they must needs be the wisest people upon earth. This thought gave me so much comfort, that I resolved to go forward until I could discover some house or village, or meet with any of the natives, leaving the two horses to discourse together as they pleased. But the first, who was a dapple gray, observing me to steal off, neighed after me in so expressive a tone, that I fancied myself to understand what he meant; whereupon I turned back, and came near him, to expect his farther commands, but concealing my fear as much as I could, for I began to be in some pain, how this adventure might terminate; and the reader will easily believe I did not much like my present situation.

The two horses came up close to me, looking with great earnestness upon my face and hands. The gray steed rubbed my hat all round with his right fore-hoof, and discomposed it so much that I was forced to adjust it better, by taking it off, and settling it again; whereat both he and his companion (who was a brown bay) appeared to be much surprised; the latter felt the lappet of my coat, and finding it to hang loose about me, they both looked with new signs of wonder. He stroked my right hand, seeming to admire the softness and colour; but he squeezed it so hard between his hoof and his pastern, that I was forced to roar; after which they both touched me with all possible tenderness. They were under great perplexity about my shoes and stockings, which they felt very often, neighing to each other, and using various gestures, not unlike those of a philosopher, when he would attempt to solve some new and difficult phenomenon.

Upon the whole, the behaviour of these animals was so orderly and rational, so acute and judicious, that I at last concluded they must needs be magicians, who had thus metamorphosed themselves upon some design, and seeing a stranger in the way, were resolved to divert themselves with him; or perhaps were really amazed at the sight of a man so very different in habit, feature, and complexion from those who might probably live in so remote a climate. Upon the strength of this reasoning, I ventured to address them in the following manner: Gentlemen, if you be conjurers, as I have good cause to believe, you can understand any language; therefore I make bold to let your worships know that I am a poor distressed Englishman, driven by his misfortunes upon your coast, and I entreat one of you, to let me ride upon his back, as if he were a real horse, to some house or village where I can be relieved. In return of which favour I will make you a present of this knife and bracelet (taking them out of my pocket). The two creatures stood silent while I spoke, seeming to listen with great attention; and when I had ended, they neighed frequently towards each other, as if they were engaged in serious conversation. I plainly observed, that their language expressed the passions very well, and the words might with little pains be resolved into an alphabet more easily than the Chinese.

I could frequently distinguish the word *Yahoo,* which was repeated by each of them several times; and although it was impossible for me to conjecture what it meant, yet while the two horses were busy in conversation, I endeavoured to practise this word upon my tongue; and as soon as they were silent, I boldly pronounced *Yahoo* in a loud voice, imitating, at the same time, as near as I could, the neighing of a horse; at which they were both visibly surprised, and the gray repeated the same word twice, as if he meant to teach me the right accent, wherein I spoke after him as well as I could, and found myself perceivably to improve every time, though very far from any degree of perfection. Then the bay tried me with a second word, much harder to be pronounced; but reducing it to the English orthography, may be spelt thus, *Houyhnhnm.* I did not succeed in this so well as the former, but after two or three farther trials, I had better fortune; and they both appeared amazed at my capacity.

After some further discourse, which I then conjectured might relate to me, the two friends took their leaves, with the same compliment of striking each other's hoof; and the gray made me signs that I should walk before him, wherein I thought it prudent to comply, till I could find a better director. When I offered to slacken my pace, he would cry *Hhuun, Hhuun;* I guessed his meaning, and gave him to understand as well as I could, that I was weary, and not able to walk faster; upon which he would stand a while to let me rest.

CHAPTER II

Having travelled about three miles, we came to a long kind of building, made of timber stuck in the ground, and wattled across; the roof was low, and covered with straw. I now began to be a little comforted, and took out some toys, which travellers usually carry for presents to the savage Indians of America and other parts, in hopes the people of the house would be thereby encouraged to receive me kindly. The horse made me a sign to go in first; it was a large room with a smooth clay floor, and a rack and manger extending the whole length on one side. There were three nags, and two mares, not eating, but some of them sitting down upon their hams, which I very much wondered at; but wondered more to see the rest employed in domestic business. These seemed but ordinary cattle; however, this con-firmed my first opinion, that a people who could so far civilize brute animals, must needs excel in wisdom all the nations of the world. The gray came in just after, and thereby prevented any ill treatment which the others might have given me. He neighed to them several times in a style of authority, and received answers.

Beyond this room there were three others, reaching the length of the house, to which you passed through three doors, opposite to each other, in the manner of a vista; we went through the second room towards the third; here the gray walked in first, beckoning me to attend: I waited in the second room, and got ready my presents for the master and mistress of the house: there were two knives, three bracelets of false pearl, a small looking-glass, and a bead necklace. The horse neighed three or four times, and I waited to hear some answers in human voice, but I heard no other returns than in the same dialect, only one or two a little shriller than his. I began to think that this house must belong to some person of great note among them, because there appeared so much ceremony before I could gain admittance. But, that a man of quality should be served all by horses, was beyond my comprehension. I feared my brain was disturbed by my sufferings and misfortunes: I roused myself, and looked about me in the room where I was left alone; this was furnished like the first, only after a more elegant manner. I rubbed my eyes often, but the same objects still occurred. I pinched my arms and sides to awake myself, hoping I might be in a dream. I then absolutely concluded, that all these appearances could be nothing else but necromancy and magic. But I had no time to pursue these reflections; for the gray horse came to the door, and made me a sign to follow him into the third room, where I saw a very comely mare, together with a colt and foal, sitting on their haunches, upon mats of straw, not unartfully made, and perfectly neat and clean.

The mare, soon after my entrance, rose from her mat, and coming up close, after having nicely observed my hands and face, gave me a most contemptuous look; then turning to the horse, I heard the word *Yahoo* often repeated betwixt them; the meaning of which word I could not then comprehend, although it were the first I had learned to pronounce; but I was soon better informed, to my everlasting mortification: for the horse beckoning me with his head, and repeating the word *Hhuun, Hhuun,* as he did upon the road, which I understood was to attend him, led me out into a kind of court, where was another building at some distance from the house. Here we entered, and I saw three of these detestable creatures, whom I first met after my landing, feeding upon roots, and the flesh of some animals, which I afterwards found to be that of asses and dogs, and now and then a cow dead by accident or disease. They were all tied by the neck with strong withes, fastened to a beam; they held their food between the claws of their fore-feet, and tore it with their teeth.

The master horse ordered a sorrel nag, one of his servants, to untie the largest of these animals, and take him into the yard. The beast and I were brought close together, and our countenances diligently compared, both by master and servant, who thereupon repeated several times the word *Yahoo*. My horror and astonishment are not to be described, when I observed in this abominable animal a perfect human figure: the face of it indeed was flat and broad, the nose depressed, the lips large, and the mouth wide. But these differences are common to all savage nations, where the lineaments of the countenance are distorted by the natives suffering their infants to lie grovelling on the earth, or by carrying them on their backs, nuzzling with their face against the mother's shoulders. The fore-feet of the Yahoo differed from my hands in nothing else but the length of the nails, the coarseness and brownness of the palms, and the hairiness on the backs. There was the same resemblance between our feet, with the same differences, which I knew very well, though the horses did not, because of my shoes and stockings; the same in every part of our bodies, except as to hairiness and colour, which I have already described.

The great difficulty that seemed to stick with the two horses, was to see the rest of my body so very different from that of a Yahoo, for which I was obliged to my clothes, whereof they had no conception. The sorrel nag offered me a root, which he held (after their manner, as we shall describe in its proper place) between his hoof and pastern; I took it in my hand, and having smelt it, returned it to him civilly as I could. He brought out of the Yahoo's kennel a piece of ass's flesh, but it smelt so offensively that I turned from it with loathing: he then threw it to the Yahoo, by whom it was greedily devoured. He afterwards showed me a wisp of hay, and a fetlock full of oats; but

I shook my head, to signify that neither of these were food for me. And indeed, I now apprehended that I must absolutely starve, if I did not get to some of my own species; for as to those filthy Yahoos, although there were few greater lovers of mankind, at that time, than myself, yet I confess I never saw any sensitive being so detestable on all accounts; and the more I came near them, the more hateful they grew, while I stayed in that country. This the master horse observed by my behaviour, and therefore sent the Yahoo back to his kennel. He then put his fore-hoof to his mouth, at which I was much surprised, although he did it with ease, and with a motion that appeared perfectly natural, and made other signs to know what I would eat; but I could not return him such an answer as he was able to apprehend; and if he had understood me, I did not see how it was possible to contrive any way for finding myself nourishment. While we were thus engaged, I observed a cow passing by, whereupon I pointed to her, and expressed a desire to let me go and milk her. This had its effect; for he led me back into the house, and ordered a mare-servant to open a room, where a good store of milk lay in earthen and wooden vessels, after a very orderly and cleanly manner. She gave me a large bowl full, of which I drank very heartily, and found myself well refreshed.

About noon I saw coming towards the house a kind of vehicle, drawn like a sledge by four Yahoos. There was in it an old steed, who seemed to be of quality; he alighted with his hind-feet forward, having by accident got a hurt in his left fore-foot. He came to dine with our horse, who received him with great civility. They dined in the best room, and had oats boiled in milk for the second course, which the old horse ate warm, but the rest cold. Their mangers were placed circular in the middle of the room, and divided into several partitions, round which they sat on their haunches upon bosses of straw. In the middle was a large rack with angles answering to every partition of the manger; so that each horse and mare ate their own hay, and their own mash of oats and milk, with much decency and regularity. The behaviour of the young colt and foal appeared very modest, and that of the master and mistress extremely cheerful and complaisant to their guest. The gray ordered me to stand by him, and much discourse passed between him and his friend concerning me, as I found by the stranger's often looking on me, and the frequent repetition of the word *Yahoo*.

I happened to wear my gloves, which the master gray observing, seemed perplexed, discovering signs of wonder what I had done to my fore-feet; he put his hoof three or four times to them, as if he would signify that I should reduce them to their former shape, which I presently did, pulling off both my gloves, and putting them into my pocket. This occasioned farther talk, and I saw the company was pleased with my behaviour, whereof I soon found the good effects. I was ordered to speak the few words I understood, and while they were at dinner the master taught me the names for oats, milk, fire, water, and some others; which I could readily pronounce after him, having from my youth a great facility in learning languages.

When dinner was done the master horse took me aside, and by signs and words made me understand the concern that he was in, that I had nothing to eat. Oats in their tongue are called *hlunnh*. This word I pronounced two or three times; for although I had refused them at first, yet upon second thoughts I considered that I could contrive to make of them a kind of bread, which might be sufficient with milk to keep me alive, till I could make my escape to some other country and to creatures of my own species. The horse immediately ordered a white mare-servant of his family to bring me a good quantity of oats in a sort of wooden tray. These I heated before the fire as well as I could, and rubbed them till the husks came off, which I made a shift to winnow from the grain; I ground and beat them between two stones, then took water, and made them into a paste or cake, which I toasted at the fire, and ate warm with milk. It was at first a very insipid diet, though common enough in many parts of Europe, but grew tolerable by time; and having been often reduced to hard fare in my life, this was not the first experiment I had made how easily nature is satisfied. And I cannot but observe, that I never had one hour's sickness while I stayed in this island. 'Tis true, I sometimes made a shift to catch a rabbit or bird by springes made of Yahoos' hairs, and I often gathered wholesome herbs, which I boiled, or ate as salads with my bread, and now and then, for a rarity, I made a little butter, and drank the whey. I was at first at a great loss for salt; but custom soon reconciled the want of it; and I am confident that the frequent use of salt among us is an effect of luxury, and was first introduced only as a provocative to drink; except where it is necessary for preserving of flesh in long voyages, or in places remote from great markets. For we observe no animal to be fond of it but man: and as to myself, when I left this country, it was a great while before I could endure the taste of it in anything that I ate.

This is enough to say upon the subject of my diet, wherewith other travellers fill their books, as if the readers were personally concerned whether we fared well or ill. However, it was necessary to mention this matter, lest the world should think it impossible that I could find sustenance for three years in such a country, and among such inhabitants.

When it grew towards evening, the master horse ordered a place for me to lodge in; it was but six yards from the house, and separated from the stable of the Yahoos. Here I got some straw, and covering myself with my own clothes, slept very sound. But I was in a short time better accommodated, as the reader shall know hereafter, when I come to treat more particularly about my way of living.

CHAPTER III

My principal endeavour was to learn the language, which my master (for so I shall henceforth call him), and his children, and every servant of his house, were desirous to teach me. For they looked upon it as a prodigy that a brute animal should discover such marks of a rational creature. I pointed to every thing and enquired the name of it, which I wrote down in my journalbook when I was alone, and corrected my bad accent by desiring those of the family to pronounce it often. In this employment a sorrel nag, one of the under servants, was ready to assist me.

In speaking they pronounce through the nose and throat, and their language approaches nearest to the High Dutch or German of any I know in Europe; but is much more graceful and significant. The Emperor Charles V made almost the same observation, when he said that if he were to speak to his horse it should be in High Dutch.

The curiosity and impatience of my master were so great, that he spent many hours of his leisure to instruct me. He was convinced (as he afterwards told me) that I must be a Yahoo, but my teachableness, civility, and cleanliness astonished him; which were qualities altogether so opposite to those animals. He was most perplexed about my clothes, reasoning sometimes with himself whether they were a part of my body; for I never pulled them off till the family were asleep, and got them on before they waked in the morning. My master was eager to learn whence I came; how I acquired those appearances of reason, which I discovered in all my actions; and to know my story from my own mouth, which he hoped he should soon do by the great proficiency I made in learning and pronouncing their words and sentences. To help my memory, I formed all I learned into the English alphabet, and writ the words down with the translations. The last after some time I ventured to do in my master's presence. It cost me much trouble to explain to him what I was doing; for the inhabitants have not the least idea of books or literature.

In about ten weeks' time I was able to understand most of his questions, and in three months could give him some tolerable answers. He was extremely curious to know from what part of the country I came, and how I was taught to imitate a rational creature; because the Yahoos (whom he saw I exactly resembled in my head, hands, and face, that were only visible), with some appearance of cunning, and the strongest disposition to mischief, were observed to be the most unteachable of all brutes. I answered that I came over the sea from a far place, with many others of my own kind, in a great hollow vessel made of the bodies of trees. That my companions forced me to land on this coast, and then left me to shift for myself. It was with some difficulty, and by the help of many signs, that I brought him to understand me. He replied, that I must needs be mistaken, or that I *said the thing which was not*. (For they have no word in their language to express lying or falsehood.) He knew it was impossible that there could be a country beyond the sea, or that a parcel of brutes could move a wooden vessel whither they pleased upon water. He was sure no Houyhnhnm alive could make such a vessel, or would trust Yahoos to manage it.

The word *Houyhnhnm*, in their tongue, signifies a *horse,* and in its etymology, *the perfection of nature.* I told my master, that I was at a loss for expression, but would improve as fast as I could; and hoped in a short time I should be able to tell him wonders: he was pleased to direct his own mare, his colt and foal, and the servants of the family, to take all opportunities of instructing me, and every day for two or three hours he was at the same pains himself. Several horses and mares of quality in the neighbourhood came often to our house upon the report spread of a wonderful Yahoo, that could speak like a Houyhnhnm, and seemed in his words and actions to discover some glimmerings of reason. These delighted to converse with me:

they put many questions, and received such answers as I was able to return. By all these advantages I made so great a progress that in five months from my arrival I understood whatever was spoke, and could express myself tolerably well.

The Houyhnhnms who came to visit my master out of a design of seeing and talking with me, could hardly believe me to be a right Yahoo, because my body had a different covering from others of my kind. They were astonished to observe me without the usual hair or skin, except on my head, face, and hands; but I discovered that secret to my master, upon an accident which happened about a fortnight before.

I have already told the reader, that every night when the family were gone to bed it was my custom to strip and cover myself with my clothes. It happened one morning early that my master sent for me by the sorrel nag, who was his valet; when he came I was fast asleep, my clothes fallen off on one side, and my shirt above my waist. I awakened at the noise he made, and observed him to deliver his message in some disorder; after which he went to my master, and in a great fright gave him a very confused account of what he had seen. This I presently discovered; for going as soon as I was dressed to pay my attendance upon his Honour, he asked me the meaning of what his servant had reported, that I was not the same thing when I slept as I appeared to be at other times; that his valet assured him, some part of me was white, some yellow, at least not so white, and some brown.

I had hitherto concealed the secret of my dress, in order to distinguish myself as much as possible from that cursed race of Yahoos; but now I found it in vain to do so any longer. Besides, I considered that my clothes and shoes would soon wear out, which already were in a declining condition, and must be supplied by some contrivance from the hides of Yahoos or some other brutes; whereby the whole secret would be known. I therefore told my master that in the country from whence I came those of my kind always covered their bodies with the hairs of certain animals prepared by art, as well for decency as to avoid the inclemencies of air, both hot and cold; of which, as to my own person, I would give him immediate conviction, if he pleased to command me; only desiring his excuse, if I did not expose those parts that nature taught us to conceal. He said my discourse was all very strange, but especially the last part; for he could not understand why nature should teach us to conceal what nature had given. That neither himself nor family were ashamed of any parts of their bodies; but however I might do as I pleased. Whereupon I first unbuttoned my coat and pulled it off. I did the same with my waistcoat; I drew off my shoes, stockings, and breeches. I let my shirt down to my waist, and drew up the bottom, fastening it like a girdle about my middle to hide my nakedness.

My master observed the whole performance with great signs of curiosity and admiration. He took up all my clothes in his pastern, one piece after another, and examined them diligently; he then stroked my body very gently and looked round me several times, after which he said it was plain I must be a perfect Yahoo; but that I differed very much from the rest of my species, in the softness and whiteness and smoothness of my skin, my want of hair in several parts of my body, the shape and shortness of my claws behind and before, and my affectation of walking continually on my two hinder-feet. He desired to see no more, and gave me leave to put on my clothes again, for I was shuddering with cold.

I expressed my uneasiness at his giving me so often the appellation of Yahoo, an odious animal for which I had so utter a hatred and contempt. I begged he would forbear applying that word to me, and take the same order in his family, and among his friends whom he suffered to see me. I requested likewise that the secret of my having a false covering to my body might be known to none but himself, at least as long as my present clothing should last; for as to what the sorrel nag his valet had observed, his Honour might command him to conceal it.

All this my master very graciously consented to, and thus the secret was kept till my clothes began to wear out, which I was forced to supply by several contrivances that shall hereafter be mentioned. In the meantime he desired I would go on with my utmost diligence to learn their language, because he was more astonished at my capacity for speech and reason than at the figure of my body, whether it were covered or no; adding that he waited with some impatience to hear the wonders which I promised to tell him.

From thenceforward he doubled the pains he had been at to instruct me; he brought me into all company, and made them treat me with civility, because, as he told them privately, this would put me into good humour and make me more diverting.

Every day when I waited on him, beside the trouble he was at in teaching, he would ask me several questions concerning myself, which I answered as well as I could; and by these means he had already received some general ideas, though very imperfect. It would be tedious to relate the several steps by which I advanced to a more regular conversation: but the first account I gave of myself in any order and length, was to this purpose:

That I came from a very far country, as I already had attempted to tell him, with about fifty more of my own species; that we travelled upon the seas, in a great hollow vessel made of wood, and larger than his Honour's house. I described the ship to him in the best terms I could, and explained by the help of my handkerchief displayed, how it was driven forward by the wind. That upon a quarrel among us, I was set on shore on this coast, where I walked forward without knowing whither, till he delivered me from the persecution of those execrable Yahoos. He asked me who made the ship, and how it was possible that the Houyhnhnms of my country would leave it to the management of brutes? My answer was that I durst proceed no further in my relation, unless he would give me his word and honour that he would not be offended, and then I would tell him the wonders I had so often promised. He agreed; and I went on by assuring him that the ship was made by creatures like myself, who in all countries I had travelled, as well as in my own, were the only governing, rational animals; and that upon my arrival hither I was as much astonished to see the Houyhnhnms act like rational beings, as he or his friends could be in finding some marks of reason in a creature he was pleased to call a Yahoo, to which I owned my resemblance in every part, but could not account for their degenerate and brutal nature. I said farther that if good fortune ever restored me to my native country, to relate my travels hither, as I resolved to do, every body would believe that I *said the thing which was not;* that I invented the story out of my own head; and with all possible respect to himself, his family and friends, and under his promise of not being offended, our countrymen would hardly think it probable, that a Houyhnhnm should be the presiding creature of a nation, and a Yahoo the brute.

CHAPTER IV

My master heard me with great appearances of uneasiness in his countenance, because *doubting,* or *not believing,* are so little known in this country, that the inhabitants cannot tell how to behave themselves under such circumstances. And I remember in frequent discourses with my master concerning the nature of manhood in other parts of the world, having occasion to talk of *lying* and *false representation,* it was with much difficulty that he comprehended what I meant, although he had otherwise a most acute judgment. For he argued thus: that the use of speech was to make us understand one another, and to receive information of facts; now if one *said the thing which was not,* these ends were defeated; because I cannot properly be said to understand him; and I am so far from receiving information, that he leaves me worse than in ignorance, for I am led to believe a thing black when it is white, and short when it is long. And these were all the notions he had concerning that faculty of *lying,* so perfectly well understood among human creatures.

To return from this digression; when I asserted that the Yahoos were the only governing animals in my country, which my master said was altogether past his conception, he desired to know whether we had Houyhnhnms among us, and what was their employment: I told him we had great numbers, that in summer they grazed in the fields, and in winter were kept in houses, with hay and oats, where Yahoo servants were employed to rub their skins smooth, comb their manes, pick their feet, serve them with food, and make their beds. I understand you well, said my master, it is now very plain, from all you have spoken, that whatever share of reason the Yahoos pretend to, the Houhynhnms are your masters; I heartily wish our Yahoos would be so tractable. I begged his Honour would please to excuse me from proceeding any farther, because I was very certain that the account he expected from me would be highly displeasing. But he insisted in commanding me to let him know the best and the worst: I told him he should be obeyed. I owned that the Houyhnhnms among us, whom we called horses, were the most generous and comely animals we had, that they excelled in strength and swiftness; and when they belonged to persons of quality, employed in travelling, racing, or drawing chariots, they were treated with much kindness and care, till they fell into disease or became foundered in the feet; and then they were sold, and used to all kind of drudgery till they died; after which their skins were stripped and sold for what they were worth, and their bodies left to be devoured by dogs and birds of prey. But the common race of horses had not so good fortune, being kept by farmers and carriers, and other mean people, who put them to great labour, and fed them worse. I described, as well as I could, our way of riding, the shape and use of a bridle, a saddle, a spur, and a whip, of harness and wheels. I added that we fastened plates of a certain hard substance called iron at the bottom of their feet, to preserve their hooves from being broken by the stony ways on which we often travelled.

My master, after some expressions of great indignation, wondered how we dared to venture upon a Houyhnhnm's back, for he was sure that the weakest servant in his house would be able to shake off the stongest Yahoo, or by lying down and rolling on his back squeeze the brute to death. I answered that our horses were trained up from three or four years old to the several uses we intended them for; that if any of them proved intolerably vicious, they were employed for carriages; that they were severely beaten while they were young, for any mischievous tricks; that the males, designed for common use of riding or draught, were generally castrated about two years after their birth, to take down their spirits and make them more tame and gentle; that they were indeed sensible of rewards and punishments; but his Honour would please to consider, that they had not the least tincture of reason any more than the Yahoos in this country.

It put me to the pains of many circumlocutions to give my master a right idea of what I spoke; for their language doth not abound in variety of words, because their wants and passions were fewer than among us. But it is impossible to represent his noble resentment at our savage treatment of the Houyhnhnm race, particularly after I had explained the manner and use of castrating horses among us, to hinder them from propagating their kind, and to render them more servile. He said if it were possible there could be any country where Yahoos alone were endued with reason, they certainly must be the governing animal, because reason will in time always prevail against brutal strength. But considering the frame of our bodies, and especially of mine, he thought no creature of equal bulk was so ill contrived, for employing that reason in the common offices of life; where-upon he desired to know whether those among whom I lived resembled me or the Yahoos of his country. I assured him, that I was as well shaped as most of my age; but the younger and the females were much more soft and tender, and the skins of the latter generally as white as milk. He said I differed indeed from other Yahoos, being much more cleanly, and not altogether so deformed, but in point of real advantage he thought I differed for the worse. That my nails were of no use either to my fore or hinder-feet; as to my fore-feet, he could not properly call them by that name, for he never observed me to walk upon them; that they were too soft to bear the ground; that I generally went with them uncovered, neither was the covering I sometimes wore on them of the same shape or so strong as that on my feet behind. That I could not walk with any security, for if either of my hinder-feet slipped, I must inevitably fall. He then began to find fault with other parts of my body, the flatness of my face, the prominence of my nose, my eyes placed directly in front, so that I could not look on either side without turning my head; that I was not able to feed myself without lifting one of my fore-feet to my mouth; and therefore nature had placed those joints to answer that necessity. He knew not what could be the use of those several clefts and divisions in my feet behind; that these were too soft to bear the hardness and sharpness of stones without a covering made from the skin of some other brute; that my whole body wanted a fence against heat and cold, which I was forced to put on and off every day with tediousness and trouble. And lastly that he observed every animal in this country naturally to abhor the Yahoos, whom the weaker avoided and the stronger drove from them. So that supposing us to have the gift of reason, he could not see how it were possible to cure that natural antipathy which every creature discovered against us; nor consequently, how we could tame and render them serviceable. However, he would (as he said) debate the matter no farther, because he was more desirous to know my own story, the country where I was born, and the several actions and events of my life before I came hither.

I assured him how extremely desirous I was that he should be satisfied on every point; but I doubted much whether it would be possible for me to explain myself on several subjects whereof his Honour could have no conception, because I saw nothing in his country to which I could resemble them. That however I would do my best, and strive to express myself by similitudes, humbly desiring his assistance when I wanted proper words; which he was pleased to promise me.

I said my birth was of honest parents in an island called England, which was remote from this country, as many days' journey as the strongest of his Honour's servants could travel in the annual course of the sun. That I was bred a surgeon, whose trade it is to cure wounds and hurts in the body, got by accident or violence; that my country was governed by a female man, whom we called a Queen. That I left it to get riches, whereby I might maintain myself and family when I should return. That in my last voyage I was Commander of the ship, and had about fifty Yahoos under me, many of which died at sea, and I was forced to supply them by others picked out from several nations. That our ship was twice in danger of being sunk; the first time by a great storm, and the second, by striking against a rock. Here my master interposed, by asking me how I could persuade strangers out of different countries to venture with me, after the losses I had sustained, and the hazards I had run. I said they were fellows of desperate fortunes, forced to fly from the places of their birth, on account of their poverty or their crimes. Some were undone by lawsuits; others spent all they had in drinking, whoring, and gaming; others fled for treason; many for murder, theft, poisoning, robbery, perjury, forgery, coining false money, for committing rapes or sodomy, for flying from their colours, or deserting to the enemy, and most of them had broken prison;

none of these durst return to their native countries for fear of being hanged, or of starving in a jail; and therefore were under the necessity of seeking livelihood in other places.

During this discourse my master was pleased to interrupt me several times; I had made use of many circumlocutions in describing to him the nature of the several crimes, for which most of our crew had been forced to fly their country. This labour took up several days' conversation before he was able to comprehend me. He was wholly at a loss to know what could be the use or necessity of practising those vices. To clear up which I endeavoured to give some ideas of the desire of power and riches, of the terrible effects of lust, intemperance, malice, and envy. All this I was forced to define and describe by putting of cases, and making of suppositions. After which, like one whose imagination was struck with something never seen or heard of before, he would lift up his eyes with amazement and indignation. Power, government, war, law, punishment, and a thousand other things had no terms wherein that language could express them, which made the difficulty almost insuperable to give my master any conception of what I meant. But being of an excellent understanding, much improved by contemplation and converse, he at last arrived at a competent knowledge of what human nature in our parts of the world is capable to perform, and desired I would give him some particular account of that land which we call Europe, but especially of my own country.

CHAPTER V

The reader may please to observe, that the following extract of many conversations I had with my master, contains a summary of the most material points which were discoursed at several times for above two years; his Honour often desiring fuller satisfaction as I farther improved in the Houyhnhnm tongue.

I laid before him, as well as I could, the whole state of Europe; I discoursed of trade and manufactures, of arts and sciences; and the answers I gave to all the questions he made, as they arose upon several subjects, were a fund of conversation not to be exhausted. But I shall here only set down the substance of what passed between us concerning my own country, reducing it into order as well as I can, without any regard to time or other circumstances, while I strictly adhere to truth. My only concern is that I shall hardly be able to do justice to my master's arguments and expressions, which must needs suffer by my want of capacity, as well as by a translation into our barbarous English.

In obedience therefore to his Honour's commands, I related to him the Revolution under the Prince of Orange; the long war with France entered into by the said prince, and renewed by his successor the present Queen, wherein the greatest powers of Christendom were engaged, and which still continued: I computed at his request that about a million of Yahoos might have been killed in the whole progress of it, and perhaps a hundred or more cities taken, and thrice as many ships burnt or sunk.

He asked me what were the usual causes or motives that made one country go to war with another. I answered they were innumerable, but I should only mention a few of the chief. Sometimes the ambition of princes, who never think they have land or people enough to govern; sometimes the corruption of ministers, who engage their master in a war in order to stifle or divert the clamour of the subjects against their evil administration. Difference in opinions hath cost many millions of lives: for instance, whether flesh be bread, or bread be flesh; whether the juice of a certain berry be blood or wine; whether whistling be a vice or a virtue; whether it be better to kiss a post, or throw it into the fire; what is the best colour for a coat, whether black, white, red, or gray; and whether it should be long or short, narrow or wide, dirty or clean; with many more. Neither are any wars so furious and bloody, or of so long continuance, as those occasioned by difference in opinion, especially if it be in things indifferent.

Sometimes the quarrel between two princes is to decide which of them shall dispossess a third of his dominions, where neither of them pretend to any right. Sometimes one prince quarrelleth with another, for fear the other should quarrel with him. Sometimes a war is entered upon, because the enemy is too strong, and sometimes because he is too weak. Sometimes our neighbours want the things which we have, or have the things which we want; and we both fight, till they take ours or give us theirs. It is a very justifiable cause of a war to invade a country after the people have been wasted by famine, destroyed by pestilence, or embroiled by factions among themselves. It is justifiable to enter into war against our nearest ally, when one of his towns lies convenient for us, or a territory of land, that would render our dominions round and complete. If a prince sends forces into a nation were the people are poor and ignorant, he may lawfully put half of them to death, and make slaves of the rest, in order to civilize and reduce them from their barbarous way of living. It is a very kingly, honourable, and frequent practice, when one prince desires the assistance of another to secure him against an invasion, that the assistant, when he hath driven out the invader, should seize on the dominions himself, and kill, imprison, or banish the prince he came to relieve. Alliance by blood or marriage is a frequent cause of war between princes; and the nearer the kindred is, the greater is their disposition to quarrel: poor nations are hungry, and rich nations are proud; and pride and hunger will ever be at variance. For these reasons, the trade of a soldier is held the most honourable of all others; because a soldier is a Yahoo hired to kill in cold blood as many of his own species, who have never offended him, as possibly he can.

There is likewise a kind of beggarly princes in Europe, not able to make war by themselves, who hire out their troops to richer nations, for so much a day to each man; of which they keep three fourths to themselves, and it is the best part of their maintenance; such are those in Germany and other northern parts of Europe.

What you have told me (said my master) upon the subject of war, does indeed discover most admirably the effects of that reason you pretend to: however, it is happy that the shame is greater than the danger; and that nature hath left you utterly uncapable of doing much mischief.

For your mouths lying flat with your faces, you can hardly bite each other to any purpose, unless by consent. Then as to the claws upon your feet before and behind, they are so short and tender, that one of our Yahoos would drive a dozen of yours before him. And therefore in recounting the numbers of those who have been killed in battle, I cannot but think that you have *said the thing which is not.*

I could not forbear shaking my head and smiling a little at his ignorance. And being no stranger to the art of war, I gave him a description of cannons, culverins, muskets, carabines, pistols, bullets, powder, swords, bayonets, battles, sieges, retreats, attacks, undermines, countermines, bombardments, sea fights; ships sunk with a thousand men, twenty thousand killed on each side; dying groans, limbs flying in the air, smoke, noise, confusion, trampling to death under horses' feet; flight, pursuit, victory; fields strewed with carcasses left for food to dogs, and wolves, and birds of prey; plundering, stripping, ravishing, burning, and destroying. And to set forth the valour of my own dear countrymen, I assured him that I had seen them blow up a hundred enemies at once in a siege, and as many in a ship, and beheld the dead bodies come down in pieces from the clouds, to the great diversion of the spectators.

I was going on to more particulars, when my master commanded me silence. He said whoever understood the nature of Yahoos might easily believe it possible for so vile an animal to be capable of every action I had named, if their strength and cunning equalled their malice. But as my discourse had increased his abhorrence of the whole species, so he found it gave him a disturbance in his mind, to which he was wholly a stranger before. He thought his ears being used to such abominable words, might by degrees admit them with less detestation. That although he hated the Yahoos of this country, yet he no more blamed them for their odious qualities, than he did a *gnnayh* (a bird of prey) for its cruelty, or a sharp stone for cutting his hoof. But when a creature pretending to reason could be capable of such enormities, he dreaded lest the corruption of that faculty might be worse than brutality itself. He seemed therefore confident, that instead of reason, we were only possessed of some quality fitted to increase our natural vices; as the reflection from a troubled stream returns the image of an ill-shapen body, not only larger, but more distorted.

He added, that he had heard too much upon the subject of war, both in this and some former discourses. There was another point which a little perplexed him at present. I had informed him, that some of our crew left their country on account of being ruined by *Law;* that I had already explained the meaning of the word; but he was at a loss how it should come to pass, that the law which was intended for every man's preservation, should be any man's ruin. Therefore he desired to be farther satisfied what I meant by law, and the dispensers thereof, according to the present practice in my own country; because he thought nature and reason were sufficient guides for a reasonable animal, as we pretended to be, in showing us what we ought to do, and what to avoid.

I assured his Honour that law was a science wherein I had not much conversed, further than by employing advocates, in vain, upon some injustices that had been done me: however, I would give him all the satisfaction I was able.

I said there was a society of men among us, bred up from their youth in the art of proving by words multiplied for the purpose, that white is black, and black is white, according as they are paid. To this society all the rest of the people are slaves. For example, if my neighbour hath a mind to my cow, he hires a lawyer to prove that he ought to have my cow from me. I must then hire another to defend my right, it being against all rules of law that any man should be allowed to speak for himself. Now in this case I who am the right owner lie under two great disadvantages. First, my lawyer, being practised almost from his cradle in defending falsehood, is quite out of his element when he would be an advocate for justice, which as an office unnatural, he always attempts with ill-will. The second disadvantage is that my lawyer must proceed with great caution, or else he will be reprimanded by the judges, and abhorred by his brethren, as one that would lessen the practise of the law. And therefore I have but two methods to preserve my cow. The first is to gain over my adversary's lawyer with a double fee, who will then betray his client by insinuating that he hath justice on his side. The second way is for my lawyer to make my cause appear as unjust as he can, by allowing the cow to belong to my adversary: and this, if it be skilfully done, will certainly bespeak the favour of the bench.

Now, your Honour is to know that these judges are persons appointed to decide all controversies of property, as well as for the trial of criminals, and picked out from the most dexterous lawyers, who are grown old or lazy, and having been biassed all their lives against truth and equity, are under such a fatal necessity of favouring fraud, perjury, and oppression, that I have known several of them to refuse a large bribe from the side where justice lay, rather than injure the faculty, by doing any thing unbecoming their nature or their office.

It is a maxim among these lawyers, that whatever hath been done before may legally be done again: and therefore they take special care to record all the decisions formerly made against common justice and the general reason of mankind. These, under the name of *precedents,* they produce as authorities, to justify the most iniquitous opinions; and the judges never fail of directing accordingly.

In pleading they studiously avoid entering into the merits of the cause, but are loud, violent, and tedious in dwelling upon all circumstances which are not to the purpose. For instance, in the case already mentioned, they never desire to know what claim or title my adversary hath to my cow; but whether the said cow were red or black, her horns long or short, whether the field I graze her in be round or square, whether she was milked at home or abroad, what diseases she is subject to, and the like; after which they consult precedents, adjourn the cause from time to time, and in ten, twenty, or thirty years, come to an issue.

It is likewise to be observed, that this society hath a peculiar cant and jargon of their own, that no other mortal can understand, and wherein all their laws are written, which they take special care to multiply; whereby they have wholly confounded the very essence of truth and falsehood, or right and wrong; so that it will take thirty years to decide whether the field left me by my ancestors for six generations belongs to me, or to a stranger three hundred miles off.

In the trial of persons accused for crimes against the state the method is much more short and commendable: the judge first sends to sound the disposition of those in power, after which he can easily hang or save the criminal, strictly preserving all due forms of law.

Here my master interposing, said it was a pity that creatures endowed with such prodigious abilities of mind as these lawyers, by the description I gave of them, must certainly be, were not rather encouraged to be instructors of others in wisdom and knowledge. In answer to which I assured his Honour that in all points out of their own trade, they were the most ignorant and stupid generation among us, the most despicable in common conversation, avowed enemies to all knowledge and learning, and equally disposed to pervert the general reason of mankind in every other subject of discourse, as in that of their own profession.

CHAPTER VI

My master was yet wholly at a loss to understand what motives could incite this race of lawyers to perplex, disquiet, and weary themselves, and engage in a confederacy of injustice, merely for the sake of injuring their fellow-animals; neither could he comprehend what I meant in saying they did it for hire. Whereupon I was at much pains to describe to him the use of money, the materials it was made of, and the value of the metals; that when a Yahoo had got a great store of this precious substance, he was able to purchase whatever he had a mind to; the finest clothing, the noblest houses, great tracts of land, the most costly meats and drinks, and have his choice of the most beautiful females. Therefore since money alone was able to perform all these feats, our Yahoos thought they could never have enough of it to spend or save, as they found themselves inclined from their natural bent either to profusion or avarice. That the rich man enjoyed the fruit of the poor man's labour, and the latter were a thousand to one in proportion to the former. That the bulk of our people were forced to live miserably, by labouring every day for small wages to make a few live plentifully. I enlarged myself much on these and many other particulars to the same purpose; but his Honour was still to seek; for he went upon a supposition that all animals had a title to their share in the productions of the earth, and especially those who presided over the rest. Therefore he desired I would let him know what these costly meats were, and how any of us happened to want them. Whereupon I enumerated as many sorts as came into my head, with the various methods of dressing them, which could not be done without sending vessels by sea to every part of the world, as well for liquors to drink, as for sauces, and innumerable other conveniences. I assured him that this whole globe of earth must be at least three times gone round, before one of our better female Yahoos could get her breakfast or a cup to put it in. He said that must needs be a miserable country which cannot furnish food for its own inhabitants. But what he chiefly wondered at, was how such vast tracts of ground as I described should be wholly without fresh water, and the people put to the necessity of sending over the sea for drink. I replied that England (the dear place of my nativity) was computed to produce three times the quantity of food, more than its inhabitants are able to consume, as well as liquors extracted from grain, or pressed out of the fruit of certain trees, which made excellent drink, and the same proportion in every other convenience of life. But, in order to feed the luxury and intemperance of the males, and the vanity of the females, we sent away the greatest part of our necessary things to other countries, from whence in return we brought the materials of diseases, folly, and vice, to spend among ourselves. Hence it follows of necessity that vast numbers of our people are compelled to seek their livelihood by begging, robbing, stealing, cheating, pimping, forswearing, flattering, suborning, forging, gaming, lying, fawning, hectoring, voting, scribbling, star-gazing, poisoning, whoring, canting, libelling, freethinking, and the like occupations: every one of which terms, I was at much pains to make him understand.

That wine was not imported among us from foreign countries, to supply the want of water or other drinks, but because it was a sort of liquid which made us merry by putting us out of our senses, diverted all melancholy thoughts, begat wild extravagant imaginations in the brain, raised our hopes, and banished our fears, suspended every office of reason for a time, and deprived us of the use of our limbs, till we fell into a profound sleep; although it must be confessed, that we always awaked sick and dispirited and that the use of this liquor filled us with diseases, which made our lives uncomfortable and short.

But beside all this, the bulk of our people supported themselves by furnishing the necessities or conveniences of life to the rich, and to each other. For instance, when I am at home and dressed as I ought to be, I carry on my body the workmanship of a hundred tradesmen; the building and furniture of my house employ as many more, and five times the number to adorn my wife.

I was going on to tell him of another sort of people, who get their livelihood by attending the sick, having upon some occassions informed his Honour that many of my crew had died of diseases. But here it was with the utmost difficulty that I brought him to apprehend what I meant. He could easily conceive that a Houyhnhnm grew weak and heavy a few days before his death, or by some accident might hurt a limb. But that nature, who works all things to perfection, should suffer any pains to breed in our bodies, he thought impossible, and desired to know the reason of so unaccountable an evil. I told him we fed on a thousand things which operated contrary to each other; that we ate when we were not hungry, and drank without the provocation of thirst; that we sat whole nights drinking strong liquors without eating a bit, which disposed us to sloth, inflamed our bodies, and precipitated or prevented digestion. That prostitute female Yahoos acquired a certain malady, which bred rottenness in the bones of those who fell into their embraces; that this and many other diseases were propagated from father to son, so that great numbers come into the world with complicated maladies upon them; that it would be endless to give him a catalogue of all diseases incident to human bodies; for they could not be fewer than five or six hundred, spread over every limb and joint; in short, every part, external and intestine, having diseases appropriated to them. To remedy which there was a sort of people bred up among us, in the profession of pretence of curing the sick. And because I had some skill in the faculty, I would in gratitude to his Honour let him know the whole mystery and method by which they proceed.

Their fundamental is that all diseases arise from repletion, from whence they conclude that a great evacuation of the body is necessary, either through the natural passage or upwards at the mouth. Their next business is from herbs, minerals, gums, oils, shells, salts, juices, seaweed, excrements, barks of trees, serpents, toads, frogs, spiders, dead men's flesh and bones, birds, beasts, and fishes, to form a composition for smell and taste the most abominable, nauseous, and detestable they can possibly contrive, which the stomach immediately rejects with loathing; and this they call a vomit; or else from the same store-house, with some other poisonous additions, they command us to take in at the orifice above or below (just as the physician then happens to be disposed) a medicine equally annoying and disgustful to the bowels; which relaxing the belly, drives down all before it, and this they call a purge or a clyster. For nature (as the physicians allege) having intended the superior anterior orifice only for the intromission of solids and liquids, and the inferior posterior for ejection, these artists ingeniously considering that in all diseases nature is forced out of her seat, therefore to replace her in it the body must be treated in a manner directly contrary, by interchanging the use of each orifice, forcing solids and liquids in at the anus, and making evacuations at the mouth.

But besides real diseases we are subject to many that are only imaginary, for which the physicians have invented imaginary cures; these have their several names, and so have the drugs that are proper for them, and with these our female Yahoos are always infested.

One great excellency in this tribe is their skill at prognostics, wherein they seldom fail; their predictions in real diseases, when they rise to any degree of malignity, generally portending death, which is always in their power, when recovery is not: and therefore, upon any unexpected signs of amendment, after they have pronounced their sentence, rather than be accused as false prophets, they know how to approve their sagacity to the world by a seasonable dose.

They are likewise of special use to husbands and wives who are grown weary of their mates, to eldest sons, to great ministers of state, and often to princes.

I had formerly upon occasion discoursed with my master upon the nature of government in general, and particularly of our own excellent constitution, deservedly the wonder and envy of the whole world. But having here accidentally mentioned a minister of state, he commanded me some time after to inform him what species of Yahoo I particularly meant by that appellation.

I told him that a First or Chief Minister of State, who was the person I intended to describe, was a creature wholly exempt from joy and grief, love and hatred, pity and anger; at least made use of no other passions but a violent desire of wealth, power, and titles; that he applies his words to all uses, except to the indication of his mind; that he never tells a truth but with an intent that you should take it for a lie; nor a lie but with a design that you should take it for a truth; that those he speaks worst of behind their backs are in the surest way of preferment; and whenever he begins to praise you to others or to yourself, you are from that day forlorn. The worst mark you can receive is a promise, especially when it is confirmed with an oath; after which every wise man retires, and gives over all hopes.

There are three methods by which a man may rise to be chief minister: the first is by knowing how with prudence to dispose of a wife, a daughter, or a sister: the second, by betraying or undermining his predecessor: and the third is by a furious zeal in public assemblies against the corruptions of the court. But a wise prince would rather choose to employ those who practise the last of these methods; because such zealots prove always the most obsequious and subservient to the will and passions of their master. That these ministers having all employments at their disposal, preserve themselves in power by bribing the majority of a senate or great council; and at last, by an expedient called an Act of Indemnity (whereof I described the nature to him) they secure themselves from after-reckonings, and retire from the public, laden with the spoils of the nation.

The palace of a chief minister is a seminary to breed up others in his own trade: the pages, lackeys, and porter, by imitating their master, become ministers of state in their several districts, and learn to excel in the three principal ingredients, of insolence, lying, and bribery. Accordingly they have a subaltern court paid to them by persons of the best rank, and sometimes by the force of dexterity and impudence arrive through several gradations to be successors to their lord.

He is usually governed by a decayed wench or favourite footman, who are the tunnels through which all graces are conveyed, and may properly be called, in the last resort, the governors of the kingdom.

One day in discourse my master, having heard me mention the nobility of my country, was pleased to make me a compliment which I could not pretend to deserve: that he was sure I must have been born of some noble family, because I far exceeded in shape, colour, and cleanliness, all the Yahoos of his nation, although I seemed to fail in strength and agility, which must be imputed to my different way of living from those other brutes; and besides I was not only endowed with the faculty of speech, but likewise with some rudiments of reason, to a degree that with all his acquaintance I passed for a prodigy.

He made me observe, that among the Houyhnhnms, the white, the sorrel, and the iron-gray, were not so exactly shaped as the bay, the dapple gray, and the black; nor born with equal talents of the mind, or a capacity to improve them; and therefore continued always in the condition of servants, without ever aspiring to match out of their own race, which in that country would be reckoned monstrous and unnatural.

I made his Honour my most humble acknowledgments for the good opinion he was pleased to conceive of me; but assured him at the same time that my birth was of the lower sort, having been born of plain honest parents, who were just able to give me a tolerable education; that nobility among us was altogether a different thing from the idea he had of it; that our young noblemen are bred from their childhood in idleness and luxury; that as soon as years will permit, they consume their vigour and contract odious diseases among lewd females; and when their fortunes are almost ruined, they marry some woman of mean birth, disagreeable person, and unsound constitution, merely for the sake of money, whom they hate and despise. That the productions of such marriages are generally scrofulous, rickety, or deformed children; by which means the family seldom continues above three generations, unless the wife takes care to provide a healthy father among her neighbours or domestics, in order to improve or continue the breed. That a weak diseased body, a meagre countenance, and sallow complexion, are the true marks of noble blood; and a healthy robust appearance is so disgraceful in a man of quality, that the world concludes his real father to have been a groom or a coachman. The imperfections of his mind run parallel with those of his body, being a composition of spleen, dullness, ignorance, caprice, sensuality, and pride.

Without the consent of this illustrious body no law can be enacted, repealed, or altered; and these have the decision of all our possessions without appeal.

CHAPTER VII

The reader may be disposed to wonder how I could prevail on myself to give so free a representation of my own species, among a race of mortals who were already too apt to conceive the vilest opinion of human kind, from that entire congruity between me and their Yahoos. But I must freely confess that the many virtues of those excellent quadrupeds placed in opposite view to human corruptions, had so far opened my eyes and enlarged my understanding, that I began to view the actions and passions of man in a very different light, and to think the honour of my own kind not worth managing; which, besides, it was impossible for me to do before a person of so acute a judgment as my master, who daily convinced me of a thousand faults in myself, whereof I had not the least perception before, and which among us would never be numbered even among human infirmities. I had likewise learned from his example an utter detestation of all falsehood or disguise, and truth appeared so amiable to me, that I determined upon sacrificing every thing to it.

Let me deal so candidly with the reader as to confess that there was yet a much stronger motive for the freedom I took in my representation of things. I had not been a year in this country before I contracted such a love and veneration for the inhabitants, that I entered on a firm resolution never to return to human kind, but to pass the rest of my life among these admirable Houyhnhnms in the contemplation and practice of every virtue; where I could have no example or incitement to vice. But it was decreed by fortune, my perpetual enemy, that so great a felicity should not fall to my share. However, it is now some comfort to reflect that in what I said of my countrymen I extenuated their faults as much as I durst before so strict an examiner, and upon every article gave as favourable a turn as the matter would bear. For indeed who is there alive that will not be swayed by his bias and partiality to the place of his birth?

I have related the substance of several conversations I had with my master, during the greatest part of the time I had the honour to be in his service, but have indeed for brevity sake omitted much more than is here set down.

When I had answered all his questions, and his curiosity seemed to be fully satisfied, he sent for me one morning early, and commanding me to sit down at some distance (an honour which he had never before conferred upon me), he said he had been very seriously considering my whole story, as far as it related both to myself and my country; that he looked upon us as a sort of animals to whose share, by what accident he could not conjecture, some small pittance of reason had fallen, whereof we made no other use than by its assistance to aggravate our natural corruptions, and to acquire new ones which nature had not given us. That we disarmed ourselves of the few abilities she had bestowed, had been very successful in multiplying our original wants, and seemed to spend our whole lives in vain endeavours to supply them by our own inventions. That as to myself, it was manifest I had neither the strength nor agility of a common Yahoo, that I walked infirmly on my hinder-feet, had found out a contrivance to make my claws of no use or defence, and to remove the hair from my chin, which was intended as a shelter from the sun and the weather. Lastly, that I could neither run with speed, nor climb trees like my brethren (as he called them) the Yahoos in this country.

That our institutions of government and law were plainly owing to our gross defects in reason, and by consequence, in virtue; because reason alone is sufficient to govern a rational creature; which was therefore a character we had no pretence to challenge, even from the account I had given of my own people; although he manifestly perceived that in order to favour them I had concealed many particulars, and often *said the thing which was not.*

He was the more confirmed in this opinion, because he observed that as I agreed in every feature of my body with other Yahoos, except where it was to my real disadvantage in point of strength, speed, and activity, the shortness of my claws, and some other particulars where nature had no part; so from the representation I had given him of our lives, our manners, and our actions, he found as near a resemblance in the disposition of our minds. He said the Yahoos were known to hate one another more than they did any different species of animals; and the reason usually assigned was the odiousness of their own shapes, which all could see in the rest, but not in themselves. He had therefore begun to think it not unwise in us to cover our bodies, and by that invention conceal many of our own deformities from each other, which would else be hardly supportable. But he now found he had been mistaken, and that the dissensions of those brutes in his country were owing to the same cause with ours, as I had described them. For if (said he) you throw among five Yahoos as much food as would be sufficient for fifty, they will, instead of eating peaceably, fall together by the ears, each single one impatient to have it all to itself; and therefore a servant was usually employed to stand by while they were feeding abroad, and those kept at home were tied at a distance from each other: that if a cow died of age or accident, before a Houyhnhnm could secure it for his own Yahoos, those in the neighbourhood would come in herds to seize it, and then would ensue such a battle as I had described, with terrible wounds made by their claws on both sides, although they seldom were able to kill one another, for want of such convenient instruments of death as we had invented. At other times the battles have been fought between the Yahoos of several neighbourhoods without any visible cause; those of one district watching all opportunities to surprise the next before they are prepared. But if they find their project hath miscarried, they return home, and, for want of enemies, engage in what I call a civil war among themselves.

That in some fields of his country there are certain shining stones of several colours, whereof the Yahoos are violently fond, and when part of these stones is fixed in the earth, as it sometimes happeneth, they will dig with their claws for whole days to get them out, then carry them away, and hide them by heaps in their kennels; but still looking round with great caution, for fear their comrades should find out their treasure. My master said he could never discover the reason of this unnatural appetite, or how these stones could be of any use to a Yahoo; but now he believed it might proceed from the same principle of avarice which I had ascribed to mankind: that he had once, by way of experiment, privately removed a heap of these stones from the place where one of his Yahoos had buried it: whereupon the sordid animal missing his treasure, by his loud lamenting brought the whole herd to the place, there miserably howled, then fell to biting and tearing the rest, began to pine away, would neither eat nor sleep nor work, till he ordered a servant privately to convey the stones into the same hole and hide them as before; which when his Yahoo had found, he presently recovered his spirits and good humour, but took good care to remove them to a better hiding-place, and hath ever since been a very serviceable brute.

My master farther assured me, which I also observed myself, that in the fields where these shining stones abound, the fiercest and most frequent battles are fought, occasioned by perpetual inroads of the neighbouring Yahoos.

He said it was common when two Yahoos discovered such a stone in a field, and were contending which of them should be the proprietor, a third would take the advantage, and carry it away from them both; which my master would needs contend to have some kind of resemblance with our suits at law; wherein I thought it for our credit not to undeceive him; since the decision he mentioned was much more equitable than many decrees among us; because the plaintiff and defendant there lost nothing beside the stone they contended for, whereas our courts of equity would never have dismissed the cause while either of them had any thing left.

My master continuing his discourse, said there was nothing that rendered the Yahoos more odious than their undistinguishing appetite to devour every thing that came in their way, whether herbs, roots, berries, the corrupted flesh of animals, or all mingled together; and it was peculiar in their temper that they were fonder of what they could get by rapine or stealth at a greater distance than much better food provided for them at home. If their prey held out, they would eat till they were ready to burst, after which nature had pointed out to them a certain root that gave them a general evacuation.

There was also another kind of root, very juicy, but somewhat rare and difficult to be found, which the Yahoos fought for with much eagerness, and would suck it with great delight; and it produced in them the same effects that wine hath upon us. It would make them sometimes hug, and sometimes tear one another; they would howl and grin, and chatter, and reel, and tumble, and then fall asleep in the dirt.

I did indeed observe that the Yahoos were the only animals in this country subject to any diseases; which, however, were much fewer than horses have among us, and contracted not by any ill-treatment they meet with, but by the nastiness and greediness of that sordid brute. Neither has their language any more than a general appellation for those maladies, which is borrowed from the name of the beast, and called *Hnea Yahoo,* or the *Yahoo's Evil,* and the cure prescribed is a mixture of their own dung and urine forcibly put down the Yahoo's throat. This I have since often known to have been taken with success, and do freely recommend it to my countrymen, for the public good, as an admirable specific against all diseases produced by repletion.

As to learning, government, arts, manufactures, and the like, my master confessed he could find little or no resemblance between the Yahoos of that country and those in ours. For he only meant to observe what parity there was in our natures. He had heard indeed that some curious Houyhnhnms observe that in most herds there was a sort of ruling Yahoo (as among us there is generally some leading or principal stag in a park), who was always more deformed in body and mischievous in disposition than any of the rest. That this leader had usually a favourite as like himself as he could get, whose employment was to lick his master's feet and posteriors, and drive the female Yahoos to his kennel; for which he was now and then rewarded with a piece of ass's flesh. This favourite is hated by the whole herd, and therefore to protect himself, keeps always near the person of his leader. He usually continues in office till a worse can be found; but the very moment he is discarded, his successor, at the head of all the Yahoos in that district, young and old, male and female, come in a body, and discharge their excrements upon him from head to foot. But how far this might be applicable to our courts and favourites, and ministers of state, my master said I could best determine.

I durst make no return to this malicious insinuation, which debased human understanding below the sagacity of a common hound, who has judgment enough to distinguish and follow the cry of the ablest dog in the pack, without being ever mistaken.

My master told me there were some qualities remarkable in the Yahoos, which he had not observed me to mention, or at least very slightly, in the accounts I had given him of human kind. He said those animals, like other brutes, had their females in common; but in this they differed, that the she Yahoo would admit the male while she was pregnant; and that the hes would quarrel and fight with the females as fiercely as with each other. Both which practices were such degrees of brutality, that no other sensitive creature ever arrived at.

Another thing he wondered at in the Yahoos was their strange disposition to nastiness and dirt, whereas there appears to be a natural love of cleanliness in all other animals. As to the former accusation, I was glad to let it pass without any reply, because I had not a word to offer upon it in defence of my species, which otherwise I certainly had done from my own inclinations.

But I could have easily vindicated human kind from the im-
putation of singularity upon the last article, if there had been
any swine in that country (as unluckily for me there were not),
which although it may be a sweeter quadruped than a Yahoo,
cannot I humbly conceive in justice pretend to more cleanliness;
and so his Honour himself must have owned, if he had seen
their filthy way of feeding, and their custom of wallowing and
sleeping in the mud.

My master likewise mentioned another quality which his servants had discovered in several Yahoos, and to him was wholly
unaccountable. He said, a fancy would sometimes take a Yahoo
to retire into a corner, to lie down and howl and groan, and
spurn away all that came near him, although he were young
and fat, and wanted neither food nor water; nor did the servants
imagine what could possibly ail him. And the only remedy they
found was to set him to hard work, after which he would
infallibly come to himself. To this I was silent out of partiality
to my own kind; yet here I could plainly discover the true seeds
of spleen, which only seizeth on the lazy, the luxurious, and the
rich; who, if they were forced to undergo the same regimen, I
would undertake for the cure.

His Honour had further observed that a female Yahoo would
often stand behind a bank or bush, to gaze on the young males
passing by, and then appear, and hide, using many antic gestures
and grimaces, at which time it was observed that she had a
most offensive smell; and when any of the males advanced,
would slowly retire, looking often back, and with a counterfeit
show of fear, run off into some convenient place where she knew
the male would follow her.

At other times if a female stranger came among them, three
or four of her own sex would get about her, and stare and
chatter, and grin, and smell her all over; and then turn off with
gestures that seemed to express contempt and disdain.

Perhaps my master might refine a little in these speculations,
which he had drawn from what he observed himself, or had

been told by others; however, I could not reflect without some amazement, and much sorrow, that the rudiments of coquetry, censure, and scandal, should have place by instinct in womankind.

I expected every moment that my master would accuse the Yahoos of those unnatural appetites in both sexes, so common among us. But nature, it seems, hath not been so expert a schoolmistress; and these politer pleasures are entirely the productions of art and reason, on our side of the globe.

CHAPTER VIII

As I ought to have understood human nature much better than I supposed it possible for my master to do, so it was easy to apply the character he gave of the Yahoos to myself and my countrymen; and I believed I could yet make farther discoveries from my own observation. I therefore often begged his favour to let me go among the herds of Yahoos in the neighbourhood, to which he always very graciously consented, being perfectly convinced that the hatred I bore those brutes would never suffer me to be corrupted by them; and his Honour ordered one of his servants, a strong sorrel nag, very honest and good-natured, to be my guard, without whose protection I durst not undertake such adventures. For I have already told the reader how much I was pestered by those odious animals upon my first arrival. And I afterwards failed very narrowly three or four times of falling into their clutches, when I happened to stray at any distance without my hanger. And I have reason to believe they had some imagination that I was of their own species, which I often assisted myself, by stripping up my sleeves, and showing my naked arms and breast in their sight, when my protector was with me. At which times they would approach as near as they durst, and imitate my actions after the manner of monkeys, but ever with great signs of hatred; as a tame jack-daw with cap and stockings is always persecuted by the wild ones, when he happens to be got among them.

They are prodigiously nimble from their infancy; however, I once caught a young male of three years old, and endeavoured by all marks of tenderness to make it quiet; but the little imp fell a squalling and scratching and biting with such violence that I was forced to let it go; and it was high time, for a whole troop of old ones came about us at the noise, but finding the cub safe (for away it ran), and my sorrel nag being by, they durst not venture near us. I observed the young animal's flesh to smell very rank, and the stink was somewhat between a weasel and a fox, but much more disagreeable. I forgot another circumstance (and perhaps I might have the reader's pardon if it were wholly omitted), that while I held the odious vermin in my hands, it voided its filthy excrements of a yellow liquid substance, all over my clothes; but by good fortune there was a small brook hard by, where I washed myself as clean as I could; although I durst not come into my master's presence, until I were sufficiently aired.

By what I could discover, the Yahoos appear to be the most unteachable of all animals, their capacities never reaching higher than to draw or carry burdens. Yet I am of opinion this defect ariseth chiefly from a perverse, restive disposition. For they are cunning, malicious, treacherous, and revengeful. They are strong and hardy, but of a cowardly spirit, and by consequence, insolent, abject, and cruel. It is observed that the red-haired of both sexes are more libidinous and mischievous than the rest, whom yet they much exceed in strength and activity.

The Houyhnhnms keep the Yahoos for present use in huts not far from the house; but the rest are sent abroad to certain fields, where they dig up roots, eat several kinds of herbs, and search about for carrion, or sometimes catch weasels and *luhimuhs* (a sort of wild rat), which they greedily devour. Nature hath taught them to dig deep holes with their nails on the side of a rising ground, wherein they lie by themselves; only the kennels of the females are larger, sufficient to hold two or three cubs.

They swim from their infancy like frogs, and are able to continue long under water, where they often take fish, which the females carry home to their young. And upon this occasion, I hope the reader will pardon my relating an odd adventure.

Being one day abroad with my protector the sorrel nag, and the weather exceeding hot, I entreated him to let me bathe in a river that was near. He consented, and I immediately stripped myself stark naked, and went down softly into the stream. It happened that a young female Yahoo, standing behind a bank, saw the whole proceeding, and inflamed by desire, as the nag and I conjectured, came running with all speed, and leaped into the water, within five yards of the place where I bathed. I was never in my life so terribly frighted; the nag was grazing at some distance, not suspecting any harm. She embraced me after a most fulsome manner; I roared as loud as I could, and the nag came galloping towards me, whereupon she quitted her grasp, with the utmost reluctancy, and leaped upon the opposite bank, where she stood gazing and howling all the time I was putting on my clothes.

This was matter of diversion to my master and his family, as well as of mortification to myself. For now I could no longer deny that I was a real Yahoo in every limb and feature, since the females had a natural propensity to me, as one of their own species. Neither was the hair of this brute of a red colour (which might have been some excuse for an appetite a little irregular), but black as a sloe, and her countenance did not make an appearance altogether so hideous as the rest of the kind; for, I think, she could not be above eleven years old.

Having lived three years in this country, the reader I suppose will expect that I should, like other travellers, give him some account of the manners and customs of its inhabitants, which it was indeed my principal study to learn.

As these noble Houyhnhnms are endowed by nature with a general disposition to all virtues, and have no conceptions or ideas of what is evil in a rational creature, so their grand maxim is to cultivate reason, and to be wholly governed by it. Neither is reason among them a point problematical as with us, where men can argue with plausibility on both sides of the question; but strikes you with immediate conviction; as it must needs do where it is not mingled, obscured, or discoloured by passion and interest. I remember it was with extreme difficulty that I could bring my master to understand the meaning of the word *opinion,* or how a point could be disputable; because reason taught us to affirm or deny only where we are certain, and beyond our knowledge we cannot do either. So that controversies, wranglings, disputes, and positiveness in false or dubious propositions, are evils unknown among the Houyhnhnms. In the like manner when I used to explain to him our several systems of natural philosophy, he would laugh that a creature pretending to reason should value itself upon the knowledge of other people's conjectures, and in things where that knowledge, if it were certain, could be of no use. Wherein he agreed entirely with the sentiments of Socrates, as Plato delivers them; which I mention as the highest honour I can do that prince of philosophers. I have often since reflected what destruction such a doctrine would make in the libraries of Europe, and how many paths to fame would be then shut up in the learned world.

Friendship and benevolence are the two principal virtues among the Houyhnhnms, and these not confined to particular objects, but universal to the whole race. For a stranger from the remotest part is equally treated with the nearest neighbour, and wherever he goes looks upon himself as at home. They preserve decency and civility in the highest degrees, but are altogether ignorant of ceremony. They have no fondness for their colts or foals, but the care they take in educating them proceeds entirely from the dictates of reason. And I observed my master to show the same affection to his neighbour's issue that he had for his own. They will have it that nature teaches them to love the whole species, and it is reason only that maketh a distinction of persons, where there is a superior degree of virtue. When the matron Houyhnhnms have produced one of each sex, they no longer accompany with their consorts, except they lose one of their issue by some casualty, which very seldom happens; but in such a case they meet again; or when the like accident befalls a person whose wife is past bearing, some other couple bestows on him one of their own colts, and then go together again till the mother is pregnant. This caution is necessary to prevent the country from being over-burthened with numbers. But the race of inferior Houyhnhnms bred up to be servants is not so strictly limited upon this article; these are allowed to produce three of each sex, to be domestics in the noble families.

In their marriages they are exactly careful to choose such colours as will not make any disagreeable mixture in the breed. Strength is chiefly valued in the male, and comeliness in the female; not upon the account of love, but to preserve the race from degenerating; for where a female happens to excel in strength, a consort is chosen with regard to comeliness. Courtship, love, presents, jointures, settlements, have no place in their thoughts, or terms whereby to express them in their language. The young couple meet and are joined, merely because it is the determination of their parents and friends: it is what they see done every day, and they look upon it as one of the necessary actions of a rational being. But the violation of marriage, or any other unchastity, was never heard of; and the married pair pass their lives with the same friendship and mutual benevolence that they bear to all others of the same species who come in their way; without jealousy, fondness, quarrelling, or discontent.

In educating the youth of both sexes, their method is admirable, and highly deserves our imitation. These are not suffered to taste a grain of oats, except upon certain days, till eighteen years old; nor milk, but very rarely; and in summer they graze two hours in the morning, and as long in the evening, which their parents likewise observe; but the servants are not allowed above half that time, and a great part of their grass is brought home, which they eat at the most convenient hours, when they can be best spared from work.

Temperance, industry, exercise, and cleanliness, are the lessons equally enjoined to the young ones of both sexes; and my master thought it monstrous in us to give the females a different kind of education from the males, except in some articles of domestic management; whereby, as he truly observed, one half of our natives were good for nothing but bringing children into the world; and to trust the care of our children to such useless animals, he said, was yet a greater instance of brutality.

But the Houyhnhnms train up their youth to strength, speed, and hardiness, by exercising them in running races up and down steep hills, and over hard stony grounds; and when they are all in a sweat, they are ordered to leap over head and ears into a pond or river. Four times a year the youth of a certain district meet to show their proficiency in running and leaping, and other feats of strength and agility; where the victor is rewarded with a song made in his or her praise. On this festival the servants drive a herd of Yahoos into the field, laden with hay and oats and milk, for a repast to the Houyhnhnms; after which these brutes are immediately driven back again, for fear of being noisome to the assembly.

Every fourth year, at the vernal equinox, there is a representative council of the whole nation, which meets in a plain about twenty miles from our house, and continues about five or six days. Here they enquire into the state and condition of the several districts; whether they abound or be deficient in hay or oats, or cows or Yahoos. And wherever there is any want (which is but seldom) it is immediately supplied by unanimous consent and contributions. Here likewise the regulation of children is settled: as, for instance, if a Houyhnhnm hath two males, he changeth one of them with another that hath two females; and when a child hath been lost by any casualty, where the mother is past breeding, it is determined what family in the district shall breed another to supply the loss.

CHAPTER IX

One of these grand assemblies was held in my time, about three months before my departure, whither my master went as the representative of our district. In this council was resumed their old debate, and indeed, the only debate which ever happened in that country; whereof my master after his return gave me a very particular account.

The question to be debated was whether the Yahoos should be exterminated from the face of the earth. One of the members for the affirmative offered several arguments of great strength and weight, alleging that as the Yahoos were the most filthy, noisome, and deformed animal which nature ever produced, so they were the most restive and indocible, mischievous and malicious: they would privately suck the teats of the Houyhnhnms' cows, kill and devour their cats, trample down their oats and grass, if they were not continually watched, and commit a thousand other extravagancies. He took notice of a general tradition, that Yahoos had not been always in that country; but that many ages ago two of these brutes appeared together upon a mountain, whether produced by the heat of the sun upon corrupted mud and slime, or from the ooze and froth of the sea, was never known. That these Yahoos engendered, and their brood in a short time grew so numerous as to over-run and infest the whole nation. That the Houyhnhnms to get rid of this evil, made a general hunting, and at last enclosed the whole herd; and destroying the elder, every Houyhnhnm kept two young ones in a kennel, and brought them to such a degree of tameness, as an animal so savage by nature can be capable of acquiring; using them for draught and carriage. That there seemed to be much truth in this tradition, and that those creatures could not be *Ylnhniamshy* (or *aborigines* of the land), because of the violent hatred the Houyhnhnms, as well as all other animals, bore them; which although their evil disposition sufficiently deserved, could never have arrived at so high a degree, if they had been aborigines, or else they would have long since been rooted out. That the inhabitants taking a fancy to use the service of the Yahoos, had very imprudently neglected to cultivate the breed of asses, which were a comely animal, easily kept, more tame and orderly, without any offensive smell, strong enough for labour, although they yield to the other in agility of body; and if their braying be no agreeable sound, it is far preferable to the horrible howlings of the Yahoos.

Several others declared their sentiments to the same purpose, when my master proposed an expedient to the assembly, whereof he had indeed borrowed the hint from me. He approved of the tradition mentioned by the honourable member who spoke before, and affirmed that the two Yahoos said to be first seen among them had been driven thither over the sea; that coming to land and being forsaken by their companions they retired to the mountains, and degenerating by degrees, became in process of time, much more savage than those of their own species in the country from whence these two originals came. The reason of his assertion was that he had now in his possession a certain wonderful Yahoo (meaning myself), which most of them had heard of, and many of them had seen. He then related to them how he first found me; that my body was all covered with an artificial composure of the skins and hairs of other animals; that I spoke in a language of my own, and had thoroughly learned theirs; that I had related to him the accidents which brought me thither; that when he saw me without my covering I was an exact Yahoo in every part, only of a whiter colour, less hairy, and with shorter claws. He added how I had endeavoured to persuade him that in my own and other countries the Yahoos acted as the governing, rational animal, and held the Houyhnhnms in servitude; that he observed in me all the qualities of a Yahoo, only a little more civilized by some tincture of reason, which however was in a degree as far inferior to the Houyhnhnm race as the Yahoos of their country were to me; that among other things I mentioned a custom we had of castrating Houyhnhnms when they were young, in order to render them tame; that the operation was easy and safe; that it was no shame to learn wisdom from brutes, as industry is taught by the ant, and building by the swallow. (For so I translate the word *lyhannh,* although it be a much larger fowl.) That this invention might be practised upon the younger Yahoos here, which, besides rendering them tractable and fitter for use, would in an age put an end to the whole species without destroying life. That in the mean time the Houyhnhnms should be exhorted to cultivate the breed of asses, which, as they are in all respects more valuable brutes, so they have this advantage, to be fit for service at five years old, which the others are not till twelve.

This was all my master thought fit to tell me at that time of what passed in the grand council. But he was pleased to conceal one particular, which related personally to myself, whereof I soon felt the unhappy effect, as the reader will know in its proper place, and from whence I date all the succeeding misfortunes of my life.

The Houyhnhnms have no letters, and consequently their knowledge is traditional. But there happening few events of any moment among a people so well united, naturally disposed to every virtue, wholly governed by reason, and cut off from all commerce with other nations, the historical part is easily preserved without burthening their memories. I have already observed that they are subject to no diseases, and therefore can

have no need of physicians. However, they have excellent med-
icines composed of herbs, to cure accidental bruises and cuts in
the pastern or frog of the foot by sharp stones, as well as other
maims and hurts in the several parts of the body.

They calculate the year by the revolution of the sun and the
moon, but use no subdivisions into weeks. They are well enough
acquainted with the motions of those two luminaries, and understand the nature of eclipses; and this is the utmost progress
of their astronomy.

In poetry they must be allowed to excel all other mortals;
wherein the justness of their similes, and the minuteness, as well
as exactness of their descriptions, are indeed inimitable. Their
verses abound very much in both of these, and usually contain
either some exalted notions of friendship and benevolence, or
the praises of those who were victors in races and other bodily
exercises. Their buildings, although very rude and simple, are
not inconvenient, but well contrived to defend them from all
injuries of cold and heat. They have a kind of tree, which at
forty years old loosens in the root, and falls with the first storm:
they grow very straight, and being pointed like stakes with a
sharp stone (for the Houyhnhnms know not the use of iron),
they stick them erect in the ground about ten inches asunder,
and then weave in oat-straw, or sometimes wattles between
them. The roof is made after the same manner, and so are the
doors.

The Houyhnhnms use the hollow part between the pastern
and the hoof of their fore-feet as we do our hands, and this
with greater dexterity than I could at first imagine. I have seen
a white mare of our family thread a needle (which I lent her
on purpose) with that joint. They milk their cows, reap their
oats, and do all the work which requires hands, in the same
manner. They have a kind of hard flints, which by grinding
against other stones, they form into instruments, that serve instead of wedges, axes, and hammers. With tools made of these

flints they likewise cut their hay and reap their oats, which there groweth naturally in several fields: the Yahoos draw home the sheaves in carriages, and the servants tread them in certain covered huts, to get out the grain, which is kept in stores. They make a rude kind of earthen and wooden vessels, and bake the former in the sun.

If they can avoid casualties, they die only of old age, and are buried in the obscurest places that can be found, their friends and relations expressing neither joy nor grief at their departure; nor does the dying person discover the least regret that he is leaving the world, any more than if he were upon returning home from a visit to one of his neighbours. I remember my master having once made an appointment with a friend and his family to come to his house upon some affair of importance; on the day fixed the mistress and her two children came very late; she made two excuses, first for her husband, who, as she said, happened that very morning to *shnuwnh*. The word is strongly expressive in their language, but not easily rendered into English; it signifies, *to retire to his first mother*. Her excuse for not coming sooner was that her husband dying late in the morning, she was a good while consulting her servants about a convenient place where his body should be laid; and I observed she behaved herself at our house as cheerfully as the rest, and died about three months later.

They live generally to seventy or seventy-five years, very seldom to fourscore: some weeks before their death they feel a gradual decay, but without pain. During this time they are much visited by their friends, because they cannot go abroad with their usual ease and satisfaction. However, about ten days before their death, which they seldom fail in computing, they return the visits that have been made them by those who are nearest in the neighbourhood, being carried in a convenient sledge drawn by Yahoos; which vehicle they use, not only upon this occasion, but when they grow old, upon long journeys, or when they are

lamed by any accident. And therefore when the dying Houyhnhnms return those visits, they take a solemn leave of their friends,
as if they were going to some remote part of the country, where
they designed to pass the rest of their lives.

I know not whether it may be worth observing that the
Houyhnhnms have no word in their language to express any
thing that is evil, except what they borrow from the deformities
or ill qualities of the Yahoos. Thus they denote the folly of a
servant, an omission of a child, a stone that cuts their feet, a
continuance of foul or unseasonable weather, and the like, by
adding to each the epithet of Yahoo. For instance, *Hhnm Yahoo,
Whnaholm Yahoo, Ynlhmndwihlma Yahoo,* and an ill-contrived
house *Ynholmhnmrohlnw Yahoo.*

I could with great pleasure enlarge further upon the manners
and virtues of this excellent people; but intending in a short
time to publish a volume by itself expressly upon that subject,
I refer the reader thither, and in the mean time, proceed to
relate my own sad catastrophe.

CHAPTER X

I had settled my little economy to my own heart's content. My
master had ordered a room to be made for me after their manner,
about six yards from the house; the sides and floors of which
I plastered with clay, and covered with rush-mats of my own
contriving; I had beaten hemp, which there grows wild, and
made of it a sort of ticking; this I filled with the feathers of
several birds I had taken with springes made of Yahoos' hairs,
and were excellent food. I had worked two chairs with my knife,
the sorrel nag helping me in the grosser and more laborious
part. When my clothes were worn to rags, I made myself others
with the skins of rabbits, and of a certain beautiful animal about
the same size, called *nnuhnoh,* the skin of which is covered with
a fine down. Of these I likewise made very tolerable stockings.

I soled my shoes with wood which I cut from a tree and fitted to the upper leather, and when this was worn out, I supplied it with the skins of Yahoos dried in the sun. I often got honey out of hollow trees, which I mingled with water, or ate with my bread. No man could more verify the truth of these two maxims. *That nature is very easily satisfied;* and *That necessity is the mother of invention.* I enjoyed perfect health of body, and tranquillity of mind; I did not feel the treachery or inconstancy of a friend, nor the injuries of a secret or open enemy. I had no occasion of bribing, flattering, or pimping to procure the favour of any great man or of his minion. I wanted no fence against fraud or oppression; here was neither physician to destroy my body, nor lawyer to ruin my fortune; no informer to watch my words and actions, or forge accusations against me for hire; here were no gibers, censurers, backbiters, pick-pockets, high-waymen, housebreakers, attorneys, bawds, buffoons, gamesters, politicians, wits, splenetics, tedious talkers, controvertists, ravishers, murderers, robbers, virtuosos; no leaders or followers of party and faction; no encouragers to vice, by seducement or examples; no dungeon, axes, gibbets, whipping-posts, or pillories; no cheating shopkeepers or mechanics; no pride, vanity, or affectation; no fops, bullies, drunkards, strolling whores, or poxes; no ranting, lewd, expensive wives; no stupid, proud pedants; no importunate, overbearing, quarrelsome, noisy, roaring, empty, conceited, swearing companions; no scoundrels, raised from the dust for the sake of their vices, or nobility thrown into it on account of their virtues; no lords, fiddlers, judges, or dancing-masters.

I had the favour of being admitted to several Houyhnhnms, who came to visit or dine with my master; where his Honour graciously suffered me to wait in the room, and listen to their discourse. Both he and his company would often descend to ask me questions, and receive my answers. I had also sometimes the honour of attending my master in his visits to others. I

never presumed to speak, except in answer to a question; and
then I did it with inward regret, because it was a loss of so
much time for improving myself; but I was infinitely delighted
with the station of a humble auditor in such conversations, where
nothing passed but what was useful, expressed in the fewest
and most significant words; where the greatest decency was observed, without the least degree of ceremony; where no person
spoke without being pleased himself, and pleasing his companions; where there was no interruption, tediousness, heat, or difference of sentiments. They have a notion that when people are
met together, a short silence doth much improve conversation:
this I found to be true; for during those little intermissions of
talk, new ideas would rise in their thoughts, which very much
enlivened the discourse. Their subjects are generally on friendship
and benevolence, or order and economy; sometimes upon the
visible operations of nature, or ancient traditions; upon the bounds
and limits of virtue; upon the unerring rules of reason, or upon
some determinations to be taken at the next great assembly;
and often upon the various excellencies of poetry. I may add
without vanity that my presence often gave them sufficient matter for discourse, because it afforded my master an occasion of
letting his friends into the history of me and my country, upon
which they were all pleased to descant in a manner not very
advantagous to human kind; and for that reason I shall not
repeat what they said: only I may be allowed to observe that
his Honour, to my great admiration, appeared to understand
the nature of Yahoos in all countries much better than myself.
He went through all our vices and follies, and discovered many
which I had never mentioned to him, by only supposing what
qualities a Yahoo of their country, with a small proportion of
reason, might be capable of exerting; and concluded, with too
much probability, how vile as well as miserable such a creature
must be.

I freely confess that all the little knowledge I have of any
value was acquired by the lectures I received from my master,

and from hearing the discourses of him and his friends; to which I should be prouder to listen than to dictate to the greatest and wisest assembly in Europe. I admired the strength, comeliness, and speed of the inhabitants; and such a constellation of virtues in such amiable persons produced in me the highest veneration. At first, indeed, I did not feel that natural awe which the Yahoos and all other animals bear towards them; but it grew upon me by degrees, much sooner than I imagined, and was mingled with a respectful love and gratitude, that they would condescend to distinguish me from the rest of my species.

When I thought of my family, my friends, my countrymen, or human race in general, I considered them as they really were, Yahoos in shape and disposition, perhaps a little more civilized, and qualified with the gift of speech, but making no other use of reason than to improve and multiply those vices whereof their brethren in this country had only the share that nature allotted them. When I happened to behold the reflection of my own form in a lake or fountain, I turned away my face in horror and detestation of myself, and could better endure the sight of a common Yahoo than of my own person. By conversing with the Houyhnhnms, and looking upon them with delight, I fell to imitate their gait and gesture, which is now grown into a habit, and my friends often tell me in a blunt way, that I trot like a horse; which, however, I take for a great compliment. Neither shall I disown that in speaking I am apt to fall into the voice and manner of the Houyhnhnms, and hear myself ridiculed on that account without the least mortification.

In the midst of all this happiness, and when I looked upon myself to be fully settled for life, my master sent for me one morning a little earlier than his usual hour. I observed by his countenance that he was in some perplexity, and at a loss how to begin what he had to speak. After a short silence he told me he did not know how I would take what he was going to say; that in the last general assembly, when the affair of the Yahoos was entered upon, the representatives had taken offence at his keeping a Yahoo (meaning myself) in his family more like a Houyhnhnm than a brute animal. That he was known frequently to converse with me, as if he could receive some advantage or pleasure in my company; that such a practice was not agreeable to reason or nature, nor a thing ever heard of before among them. The assembly did therefore exhort him, either to employ me like the rest of my species, or command me to swim back to the place from whence I came. That the first of these expedients were utterly rejected by all the Houyhnhnms who had ever seen me at his house or their own: for they alleged that because I had some rudiments of reason, added to the natural pravity of those animals, it was to be feared I might be able to seduce them into the woody and mountainous parts of the country, and bring them in troops by night to destroy the Houyhnhnms' cattle, as being naturally of the ravenous kind, and averse from labour.

My master added that he was daily pressed by the Houyhnhnms of the neighbourhood to have the assembly's exhortation executed, which he could not put off much longer. He doubted it would be impossible for me to swim to another country, and therefore wished I would contrive some sort of vehicle resembling those I had described to him, that might carry me on the sea; in which work I should have the assistance of his own servants, as well as those of his neighbours. He concluded that for his own part he could have been content to keep me in his service as long as I lived; because he found I had cured myself of some bad habits and dispositions, by endeavouring, as far as my inferior nature was capable, to imitate the Houyhnhnms.

I should here observe to the reader, that a decree of the general assembly in this country is expressed by the word *hnhloayn,* which signifies an exhortation, as near as I can render it; for they have no conception how a rational creature can be compelled, but only advised or exhorted, because no person can disobey reason without giving up his claim to be a rational creature.

I was struck with the utmost grief and despair at my master's discourse, and being unable to support the agonies I was under, I fell into a swoon at his feet; when I came to myself he told me that he concluded I had been dead (for these people are subject to no such imbecilities of nature). I answered in a faint voice that death would have been too great a happiness; that although I could not blame the assembly's exhortation, or the urgency of his friends, yet, in my weak and corrupt judgment, I thought it might consist with reason to have been less rigorous. That I could not swim a league, and probably the nearest land to theirs might be distant above a hundred; that many materials, necessary for making a small vessel to carry me off, were wholly wanting in this country, which, however, I would attempt in obedience and gratitude to his Honour, although I concluded the thing to be impossible, and therefore looked on myself as already devoted to destruction. That the certain prospect of an unnatural death was the least of my evils; for supposing I should escape with life by some strange adventure, how could I think with temper of passing my days among Yahoos, and relapsing into my old corruptions, for want of examples to lead and keep me within the paths of virtue? That I knew too well upon what solid reasons all the determinations of the wise Houyhnhnms were founded, not to be shaken by arguments of mine, a miserable Yahoo; and therefore, after presenting him with my humble thanks for the offer of his servants' assistance in making a vessel, and desiring a reasonable time for so difficult a work, I told him I would endeavour to preserve a wretched being; and if ever I returned to England, was not without hopes of being useful to my own species by celebrating the praises of the renowned Houyhnhnms, and proposing their virutes to the imitation of mankind.

My master in a few words made me a very gracious reply, allowed me the space of two months to finish my boat; and ordered the sorrel nag, my fellow-servant (for so at this distance I may presume to call him) to follow my instructions, because I told my master that his help would be sufficient, and I knew he had a tenderness for me.

In his company my first business was to go to that part of the coast where my rebellious crew had ordered me to be set on shore. I got upon a height, and looking on every side into the sea, fancied I saw a small island towards the north-east: I took out my pocket-glass, and could then clearly distinguish it about five leagues off, as I computed; but it appeared to the sorrel nag to be only a blue cloud; for as he had no conception of any country beside his own, so he could not be as expert in distinguishing remote objects at sea as we who so much converse in that element.

After I had discovered this island, I considered no farther; but resolved it should, if possible, be the first place of my banishment, leaving the consequences to fortune.

I returned home, and consulting with the sorrel nag, we went into a copse at some distance, where I with my knife, and he with a sharp flint fastened very artificially after their manner to a wooden handle, cut down several oak wattles about the thickness of a walking-staff, and some larger pieces. But I shall not trouble the reader with a particular description of my own mechanics; let it suffice to say that in six weeks' time, with the help of the sorrel nag, who performed the parts that required most labour, I finished a sort of Indian canoe, but much larger, covering it with the skins of Yahoos well stitched together, with hempen threads of my own making. My sail was likewise composed of the skins of the same animal; but I made use of the youngest I could get, the older being too tough and thick; and I likewise provided myself with four paddles. I laid in a stock of boiled flesh, of rabbits and fowls, and took with me two vessels, one filled with milk and the other with water.

I tried my canoe in a large pond near my master's house, and then corrected in it what was amiss; stopping all the chinks with Yahoos' tallow, till I found it staunch, and able to bear me and my freight. And when it was as complete as I could possibly make it, I had it drawn on a carriage very gently by Yahoos to the sea-side, under the conduct of the sorrel nag and another servant.

When all was ready, and the day came for my departure, I took leave of my master and lady and the whole family, my eyes flowing with tears, and my heart quite sunk with grief. But his Honour, out of curiosity, and perhaps (if I may speak it without vanity) partly out of kindness, was determined to see me in my canoe, and got several of his neighbouring friends to accompany him. I was forced to wait above an hour for the tide, and then observing the wind very fortunately bearing towards the island to which I intended to steer my course, I took a second leave of my master; but as I was going to prostrate myself to kiss his hoof, he did me the honour to raise it gently to my mouth. I am not ignorant how much I have been censured for mentioning this last particular. For my detractors are pleased to think it improbable that so illustrious a person should descend to give so great a mark of distinction to a creature so inferior as I. Neither have I forgot how apt some travellers are to boast of extraordinary favours they have received. But if these censurers were better acquainted with the noble and courteous disposition of the Houyhnhnms, they would soon change their opinion.

I paid my respects to the rest of the Houyhnhnms in his Honour's company; then getting into my canoe, I pushed off from shore.

CHAPTER XI

I began this desperate voyage on February 15, 1714–5, at 9 o'clock in the morning. The wind was very favourable; however, I made use at first only of my paddles; but considering I should soon be weary, and that the wind might chop about, I ventured to set up my little sail; and thus with the help of the tide I went at the rate of a league and a half an hour, as near as I could guess. My master and his friends continued on the shore till I was almost out of sight; and I often heard the sorrel nag (who always loved me) crying out, *Hnuy illa nyha majah Yahoo,* Take care of thyself, gentle Yahoo.

My design was, if possible, to discover some small island uninhabited, yet sufficient by my labour to furnish me with the necessaries of life, which I would have thought a greater happiness than to be first minister in the politest court of Europe; so horrible was the idea I conceived of returning to live in the society and under the government of Yahoos. For in such a solitude as I desired I could at least enjoy my own thoughts, and reflect with delight on the virtues of those inimitable Houyhnhnms, without any opportunity of degenerating into the vices and corruptions of my own species.

The reader may remember what I related when my crew conspired against me and confined me to my cabin. How I continued there several weeks without knowing what course we took; and when I was put ashore in the long-boat, how the sailors told me with oaths, whether true or false, that they know not in what part of the world we were. However, I did then believe us to be about ten degrees southward of the Cape of Good Hope, or about 45 degrees southern latitude, as I gathered from some general words I overheard among them, being I supposed to the south-east in their intended voyage to Madagascar. And although this were but little better than conjecture, yet I resolved to steer my course eastward, hoping to reach the south-west coast of New Holland, and perhaps some such island as I desired, lying westward of it. The wind was full west, and by six in the evening I computed I had gone eastward at least eighteen leagues, when I spied a very small island about half a league off, which I soon reached. It was nothing but a rock, with one creek, naturally arched by the force of tempests. Here I put in my canoe, and climbing up a part of the rock, I could plainly discover land to the east, extending from south to north. I lay all night in my canoe; and repeating my voyage early in the morning, I arrived in seven hours to the south-east point of New Holland. This confirmed me in the opinion I have long entertained, that the maps and charts place this country at least three degrees more to the east than it really is; which thought I communicated many years ago to my worthy friend Mr. Herman Moll, and gave him my reasons for it, although he hath rather chosen to follow other authors.

I saw no inhabitants in the place where I landed, and being unarmed, I was afraid of venturing far into the country. I found some shellfish on the shore, and ate them raw, not daring to kindle a fire, for fear of being discovered by the natives. I continued three days feeding on oysters and limpets, to save my own provisions; and I fortunately found a brook of excellent water, which gave me great relief.

On the fourth day, venturing out early a little too far, I saw twenty or thirty natives upon a height, not above five hundred yards from me. They were stark naked, men, women, and children, round a fire, as I could discover by the smoke. One of them spied me, and gave notice to the rest; five of them advanced towards me, leaving the women and children at the fire. I made what haste I could to the shore, and getting into my canoe, shoved off: the savages, observing me retreat, ran after me; and before I could get far enough into the sea, discharged an arrow, which wounded me deeply on the inside of my left knee (I shall carry the mark to my grave). I apprehended the arrow might be poisoned, and paddling out of the reach of their darts (being a calm day), I made a shift to suck the wound and dress it as well as I could.

I was at loss what to do, for I durst not return to the same landing-place, but stood to the north, and was forced to paddle;

for the wind, though very gentle, was against me, blowing north-west. As I was looking about for a secure landing-place, I saw a sail to the north-north-east, which appearing every minute more visible, I was in some doubt whether I should wait for them or no; but at last my detestation of the Yahoo race prevailed, and turning my canoe, I sailed and paddled together to the south, and got into the same creek from whence I set out in the morning, choosing rather to trust myself among these barbarians, than live with European Yahoos. I drew up my canoe as close as I could to the shore, and hid myself behind a stone by the little brook, which, as I have already said, was excellent water.

The ship came within half a league of this creek, and sent her long-boat with vessels to take in fresh water (for the place it seems was very well known), but I did not observe it till the boat was almost on shore, and it was too late to seek another hiding-place. The seamen at their landing observed my canoe, and rummaging it all over, easily conjectured that the owner could not be far off. Four of them, well armed, searched every cranny and lurking-hole, till at last they found me flat on my face behind the stone. They gazed awhile in admiration at my strange uncouth dress, my coat made of skins, my wooden-soled shoes, and my furred stockings; from whence, however, they concluded I was not a native of the place, who all go naked. One of the seamen in Portuguese bid me rise, and asked who I was. I understood that language very well, and getting upon my feet, said I was a poor Yahoo, banished from the Houy-hnhnms, and desired they would please let me depart. They admired to hear me answer them in their own tongue, and saw by my complexion I must be a European, but were at a loss to know what I meant by Yahoos and Houyhnhnms, and at the same time fell a laughing at my strange tone in speaking, which resembled the neighing of a horse. I trembled all the while between fear and hatred: I again desired leave to depart, and was gently moving to my canoe; but they laid hold of me, desiring to know what country I was of, whence I came, with many other questions. I told them I was born in England, from whence I came about five years ago, and then their country and ours were at peace. I therefore hoped they would not treat me as an enemy, since I meant them no harm, but was a poor Yahoo, seeking some desolate place where to pass the remainder of his unfortunate life.

When they began to talk, I thought I never heard or saw any thing so unnatural; for it appeared to me as monstrous as if a dog or a cow should speak in England, or a Yahoo in Houyhnhnm-land. The honest Portuguese were equally amazed at my strange dress, and the odd manner of delivering my words, which however they understood very well. They spoke to me with great humanity, and said they were sure the Captain would carry me gratis to Lisbon, from whence I might return to my own country; that two of the seamen would go back to the ship, inform the Captain of what they had seen, and receive his orders; in the mean time, unless I would give my solemn oath not to fly, they would secure me by force. I thought it best to comply with their proposal. They were very curious to know my story, but I gave them very little satisfaction; and they all conjectured that my misfortunes had impaired my reason. In two hours the boat, which went loaden with vessels of water, returned with the Captain's command to fetch me on board. I fell on my knees to preserve my liberty; but all was in vain, and the men having tied me with cords, heaved me into the boat, from whence I was taken into the ship, and from thence into the Captain's cabin.

His name was Pedro de Mendez; he was a very courteous and generous person; he entreated me to give some account of myself, and desired to know what I would eat or drink; said I should be used as well as himself, and spoke so many obliging things, that I wondered to find such civilities from a Yahoo.

However, I remained silent and sullen; I was ready to faint at the very smell of him and his men. At last I desired something to eat out of my own canoe; but he ordered me a chicken and some excellent wine, and then directed that I should be put to bed in a very clean cabin. I would not undress myself, but lay on the bed-clothes, and in half an hour stole out, when I thought the crew was at dinner, and getting to the side of the ship was going to leap into the sea, and swim for my life, rather than continue among Yahoos. But one of the seamen prevented me, and having informed the Captain, I was chained to my cabin.

After dinner Don Pedro came to me, and desired to know my reason for so desperate an attempt, assured me he only meant to do me all the service he was able, and spoke so very movingly, that at last I descended to treat him like an animal which had some little portion of reason. I gave him a very short relation of my voyage, of the conspiracy against me by my own men, of the country where they set me on shore, and of my three years' residence there. All which he looked upon as if it were a dream or a vision; whereat I took great offence, for I had quite forgot the faculty of lying, so peculiar to Yahoos in all countries where they preside, and, consequently the disposition of suspecting truth in others of their own species. I asked him whether it were the custom in his country to *say the thing that was not*. I assured him I had almost forgot what he meant by falsehood, and if I had lived a thousand years in Houyhnhnm-land, I should never have heard a lie from the meanest servant, that I was altogether indifferent whether he believed me or no, but however, in return for his favours, I would give so much allowance to the corruption of his nature as to answer any objection he would please to make, and then he might easily discover the truth.

The Captain, a wise man, after many endeavours to catch me tripping in some part of my story, at last began to have a better opinion of my veracity, and the rather, because he confessed he met with a Dutch skipper, who pretended to have landed with five others of his crew upon a certain island or continent south of New Holland, where they went for fresh water, and observed a horse driving before him several animals exactly resembling those I described under the name of Yahoos, with some other particulars, which the Captain said he had forgot; because he then concluded them all to be lies. But he added that since I professed so inviolable an attachment to truth, I must give him my word of honour to bear him company in this voyage, without attempting any thing against my life, or else he would continue me a prisoner till we arrived at Lisbon. I gave him the promise he required, but at the same time protested that I would suffer the greatest hardships rather than return to live among Yahoos.

Our voyage passed without any considerable accident. In gratitude to the Captain I sometimes sat with him at his earnest request, and strove to conceal my antipathy to human kind, although it often broke out, which he suffered to pass without observation. But the greatest part of the day I confined myself to my cabin, to avoid seeing any of the crew. The Captain had often entreated me to strip myself of my savage dress, and offered to lend me the best suit of clothes he had. This I would not be prevailed on to accept, abhorring to cover myself with any thing that had been on the back of a Yahoo. I only desired he would lend me two clean shirts, which having been washed since he wore them, I believed would not so much defile me. These I changed every second day, and washed them myself.

We arrived at Lisbon, Nov. 5, 1715. At our landing the captain forced me to cover myself with his cloak, to prevent the rabble from crowding about me. I was conveyed to his own house, and at my earnest request he led me up to the highest room backwards. I conjured him to conceal from all persons what I had told him of the Houyhnhnms, because the least hint of such a story would not only draw numbers of people to see me, but probably put me in danger of being imprisoned, or burnt by the Inquisition. The Captain persuaded me to accept a suit of clothes newly made; but I would not suffer the tailor to take my measure; however, Don Pedro being almost of my size, they fitted me well enough. He accoutred me with other necessaries all new, which I aired for twenty-four hours before I would use them.

The Captain had no wife, nor above three servants, none of which were suffered to attend at meals, and his whole deportment was so obliging, added to very good *human* understanding, that I really began to tolerate his company. He gained so far upon me that I ventured to look out of the back window. By degrees I was brought into another room, from whence I peeped into the street, but drew my head back in a fright. In a week's time he seduced me down to the door. I found my terror gradually lessened, but my hatred and contempt seemed to increase. I was at last bold enough to walk the street in his company, but kept my nose well stopped with rue, or sometimes with tobacco.

In ten days Don Pedro, to whom I had given some account of my domestic affairs, put it upon me as a matter of honour and conscience, that I ought to return to my native country, and live at home with my wife and children. He told me there was an English ship in the port just ready to sail, and he would furnish me with all things necessary. It would be tedious to repeat his arguments, and my contradictions. He said it was altogether impossible to find such a solitary island as I had desired to live in; but I might command in my own house, and pass my time in a manner as recluse as I pleased.

I complied at last, finding I could do no better. I left Lisbon the 24th day of November, in an English merchantman, but who was the master I never enquired. Don Pedro accompanied me to the ship, and lent me twenty pounds. He took kind leave of me, and embraced me at parting, which I bore as well as I could. During this last voyage I had no commerce with the master or any of his men; but pretending I was sick, kept close in my cabin. On the fifth of December, 1715, we cast anchor in the Downs about nine in the morning, and at three in the afternoon I got safe to my house at Redriff.

My wife and family received me with great surprise and joy, because they concluded me certainly dead; but I must freely confess the sight of them filled me only with hatred, disgust, and contempt, and the more by reflecting on the near alliance I had to them. For although since my unfortunate exile from the Houyhnhnm country, I had compelled myself to tolerate the sight of Yahoos, and to coverse with Don Pedro de Mendez, yet my memory and imagination were perpetually filled with the virtues and ideas of those exalted Houyhnhnms. And when I began to consider that by copulating with one of the Yahoo species I had become a parent of more, it struck me with the utmost shame, confusion, and horror.

As soon as I entered the house, my wife took me in her arms and kissed me, at which, having not been used to the touch of that odious animal for so many years, I fell in a swoon for almost an hour. At the time I am writing it is five years since my last return to England: during the first year I could not endure my wife or children in my presence, the very smell of them was intolerable; much less could I suffer them to eat in the same room. To this hour they dare not presume to touch my bread, or drink out of the same cup, neither was I ever able to let one of them take me by the hand. The first money I laid out was to buy two young stone-horses, which I keep in a good stable, and next to them the groom is my greatest favourite; for I feel my spirits revived by the smell he contracts in the stable. My horses understand me tolerably well; I converse with them at least four hours every day. They are strangers to bridle or saddle; they live in great amity with me, and friendship to each other.

CHAPTER XII

Thus, gentle reader, I have given thee a faithful history of my travels for sixteen years and above seven months; wherein I have not been so studious of ornament as truth. I could perhaps like others have astonished thee with strange improbable tales; but I rather chose to relate plain matter of fact in the simplest manner and style; because my principal design was to inform, and not to amuse thee.

It is easy for us who travel into remote countries, which are seldom visited by Englishmen or other Europeans, to form descriptions of wonderful animals both at sea and land. Whereas a traveller's chief aim should be to make men wiser and better, and to improve their minds by the bad as well as good example of what they deliver concerning foreign places.

I could heartily wish a law was enacted, that every traveller, before he were permitted to publish his voyages, should be obliged to make oath before the Lord High Chancellor that all he intended to print was absolutely true to the best of his knowledge; for then the world would no longer be deceived as it usually is, while some writers, to make their works pass the better upon the public, impose the grossest falsities on the unwary reader. I have perused several books of travels with great delight in my younger days; but having since gone over most parts of the globe, and been able to contradict many fabulous accounts from my own observation, it hath given me a great disgust against this part of reading, and some indignation to see the credulity of mankind so impudently abused. Therefore since my acquaintance were pleased to think my poor endeavours might not be acceptable to my country, I imposed on myself as a maxim, never to be swerved from, that I would *strictly adhere to truth;* neither indeed can I be ever under the least temptation to vary from it, while I retain in my mind the lectures and example of my noble master, and the other illustrious

Houyhnhnms, of whom I had so long the honour to be a humble hearer.

 —*Nec si miserum Fortuna Sinonem*
 Finxit, vanum etiam mendacemque improba finget.[1]

 I know very well how little reputation is to be got by writings which require neither genius nor learning, nor indeed any other talent except a good memory or an exact journal. I know likewise that writers of travels, like dictionary-makers, are sunk into oblivion by the weight and bulk of those who come after, and therefore lie uppermost. And it is highly probable that such travellers who shall hereafter visit the countries described in this work of mine, may, by detecting my errors (if there be any), and adding many new discoveries of their own, jostle me out of vogue, and stand in my place, making the world forget that I was ever an author. This indeed would be too great a mortification if I wrote for fame: but, as my sole intention was the PUBLIC GOOD, I cannot be altogether disappointed. For who can read of the virtues I have mentioned in the glorious Houyhnhnms, without being ashamed of his own vices, when he considers himself as the reasoning, governing animal of his country? I shall say nothing of those remote nations where Yahoos preside; among which the least corrupted are the Brobdingnagians, whose wise maxims in morality and government it would be our happiness to observe. But I forbear descanting farther, and rather leave the judicious reader to his own remarks and applications.

 I am not a little pleased that this work of mine can possibly meet with no censurers: for what objections can be made against a writer who relates only plain facts that happened in such distant countries, where we have not the least interest with respect either

---

[1] ["Though Fortune has made Sinon miserable, she has not made him untrue and a liar." —*Aeneid*]

to trade or negotiations? I have carefully avoided every fault with which common writers of travels are often too justly charged. Besides, I meddle not the least with any party, but write without passion, prejudice, or ill-will against any man or number of men whatsoever. I write for the noblest end, to inform and instruct mankind, over whom I may, without breach of modesty, pretend to some superiority, from the advantages I received by conversing so long among the most accomplished Houyhnhnms. I write without any view towards profit or praise. I never suffer a word to pass that may look like reflection, or possibly give the least offence even to those who are most ready to take it. So that I hope I may with justice pronounce myself an author perfectly blameless, against whom the tribes of answerers, considerers, observers, reflecters, detecters, remarkers, will never be able to find matter for exercising their talents.

I confess, it was whispered to me, that I was bound in duty as a subject of England, to have given in a memorial to a Secretary of State, at my first coming over; because whatever lands are discovered by a subject belong to the Crown. But I doubt whether our conquests in the countries I treat of, would be as easy as those of Ferdinando Cortez over the naked Americans. The Lilliputians I think are hardly worth the charge of a fleet and army to reduce them; and I question whether it might be prudent or safe to attempt the Brobdingnagians; or whether an English army would be much at their ease with the Flying Island over their heads. The Houyhnhnms, indeed, appear not to be so well prepared for war, a science to which they are perfect strangers, and especially against missive weapons. However, supposing myself to be a minister of state, I could never give my advice for invading them. Their prudence, unanimity, unacquaintedness with fear, and their love of their country, would amply supply all defects in the military art. Imagine twenty thousand of them breaking into the midst of a European army, confounding the ranks, overturning the carriages, battering the warriors' faces into mummy by terrible yerks from their hinder-hooves. For they would well deserve the character given to Augustus: *Recalcitrat undique tutus.* But instead of proposals for conquering that magnanimous nation, I rather wish they were in a capacity or disposition to send a sufficient number of their inhabitants for civilizing Europe, by teaching us the first principles of honour, justice, truth, temperance, public spirit, fortitude, chastity, friendship, benevolence, and fidelity. The names of all which virtues are still retained among us in most languages, and are to be met with in modern as well as ancient authors; which I am able to assert from my own small reading.

But I had another reason which made me less forward to enlarge his Majesty's dominions by my discoveries. To say the truth, I had conceived a few scruples with relation to the distributive justice of princes upon those occasions. For instance, a crew of pirates are driven by a storm they know not whither; at length a boy discovers land from the topmast, they go on shore to rob and plunder, they see a harmless people, are entertained with kindness, they give the country a new name, they take formal possession of it for their King, they set up a rotten plank or a stone for a memorial, they murder two or three dozen of the natives, bring away a couple more by force for a sample, return home, and get their pardon. Here commences a new dominion acquired with a title by *divine right.* Ships are sent with the first opportunity, the natives driven out or destroyed, their princes tortured to discover their gold, a free licence given to all acts of inhumanity and lust, the earth reeking with the blood of its inhabitants: and this execrable crew of butchers employed in so pious an expedition, is a *modern colony* set to convert and civilize an idolatrous and barbarous people.

But this description, I confess, doth by no means affect the British nation, who may be an example to the whole world for their wisdom, care, and justice in planting colonies; their liberal endowments for the advancement of religion and learning; their choice of devout and able pastors to propagate Christianity; their caution in stocking their provinces with people of sober lives and conversations from this the mother kingdom; their strict regard to the distribution of justice, in supplying the civil administration through all their colonies with officers of the greatest abilities, utter strangers to corruption; and to crown all, by sending the most vigilant and virtuous governors, who have no other views than the happiness of the people over whom they preside, and the honour of the King their master.

But, as those countries which I have described do not appear to have any desire of being conquered, and enslaved, murdered, or driven out by colonies, nor abound either in gold, silver, sugar, or tobacco; I did humbly conceive they were by no means proper objects of our zeal, our valour, or our interest. However, if those whom it more concerns think fit to be of another opinion, I am ready to depose, when I shall be lawfully called, that no European did ever visit these countries before me. I mean, if the inhabitants ought to be believed; unless a dispute may arise about the two Yahoos, said to have been seen many ages ago in a mountain in Houyhnhnm-land, from whence the opinion is, that the race of those brutes hath descended; and these, for anything I know, may have been English, which indeed I was apt to suspect from the lineaments of their posterity's countenances, although very much defaced. But, how far that will go to make out a title, I leave to the learned in colony-law.

But as to the formality of taking possession in my Sovereign's name, it never came once into my thoughts; and if it had, yet as my affairs then stood, I should perhaps in point of prudence and self-preservation have put it off to a better opportunity.

Having thus answered the only objection that can ever be raised against me as a traveller, I here take a final leave of all my courteous readers, and return to enjoy my own speculations in my little garden at Redriff, to apply those excellent lessons of virtue which I learned among the Houyhnhnms, to instruct the Yahoos of my own family as far as I shall find them docible animals; to behold my figure often in a glass, and thus if possible habituate myself by time to tolerate the sight of a human creature; to lament the brutality of Houyhnhnms in my own country, but always treat their persons with respect, for the sake of my noble master, his family, his friends, and the whole Houyhnhnm race, whom these of ours have the honour to resemble in all their lineaments, however their intellectuals came to degenerate.

I began last week to permit my wife to sit at dinner with me, at the farthest end of a long table, and to answer (but with the utmost brevity) the few questions I ask her. Yet the smell of a Yahoo continuing very offensive, I always keep my nose well stopped with rue, lavender, or tobacco leaves. And although it be hard for a man late in life to remove old habits, I am not altogether out of hopes in some time to suffer a neighbour Yahoo in my company, without the apprehensions I am yet under of his teeth or his claws.

My reconcilement to the Yahoo-kind in general might not be so difficult, if they would be content with those vices and follies only which nature hath entitled them to. I am not in the least provoked at the sight of a lawyer, a pick-pocket, a colonel, a fool, a lord, a gamester, a politician, a whore-master, a physician, an evidence, a suborner, an attorney, a traitor, or the like; this is all according to the due course of things: but when I behold a lump of deformity and diseases both in body and mind, smitten with *pride,* it immediately breaks all the measures of my patience; neither shall I be ever able to comprehend how such an animal and such a vice could tally together. The wise and virtuous Houyhnhnms, who abound in all excellencies that can adorn a rational creature, have no name for this vice in their language, which hath no terms to express any thing that is evil, except those whereby they describe the detestable qualities of their Yahoos; among which they were not able to distinguish this of pride, for want of thoroughly understanding human nature, as it showeth itself in other countries, where that animal presides. But I, who had more experience, could plainly observe some rudiments of it among the wild Yahoos.

But the Houyhnhnms, who live under the government of reason, are no more proud of the good qualities they possess, than I should be for not wanting a leg or an arm, which no man in his wits would boast of, although he must be miserable without them. I dwell the longer upon this subject from the desire I have to make the society of an English Yahoo by any means not insupportable; and therefore I here entreat those who have any tincture of this absurd vice, that they will not presume to come in my sight.

HENRY DAVID THOREAU was born in Concord, Massachusetts, in 1817. His friend Ralph Waldo Emerson remarked, ". . . few lives contain so much renunciation." Solitude and nature inspired Thoreau; he was a "self-appointed inspector of snow-storms and rain-storms" whose journal—devoted to nature, philosophy, and poetry—spanned thirty-two volumes. At Harvard College, where he studied classics, Thoreau objected to his "many and noisy neighbors." He resigned from his first teaching position because he opposed corporal punishment. "Great thoughts hallow any labor," wrote Thoreau, defending his many odd jobs that followed. He served as Emerson's handyman, making gloves for Emerson's chickens to protect the garden from their claws. He secluded himself at Walden Pond from 1845–47, writing *Walden* (1854). Thoreau was jailed for not paying his poll tax; *Civil Disobedience* (1849) is his account of this. Thoreau's books sold poorly. But "snakes coiled round his leg; the fishes swam into his hand . . . he pulled the woodchuck out of its hole by the tail, and took the foxes under his protection. . . ." Thoreau died in 1862.

From *The Portable Thoreau,* edited by Carl Bode. Publisher: Penguin Books, 1983.

Civil Disobedience

I heartily accept the motto—"That government is best which governs least"; and I should like to see it acted up to more rapidly and systematically. Carried out, it finally amounts to this, which also I believe—"That government is best which governs not at all"; and when men are prepared for it, that will be the kind of government which they will have. Government is at best but an expedient; but most governments are usually, and all governments are sometimes, inexpedient. The objections which have been brought against a standing army, and they are many and weighty, and deserve to prevail, may also at last be brought against a standing government. The standing army is only an arm of the standing government. The government itself, which is only the mode which the people have chosen to execute their will, is equally liable to be abused and perverted before the people can act through it. Witness the present Mexican war, the work of comparatively a few individuals using the standing government as their tool; for, in the outset, the people would not have consented to this measure.

This American government—what is it but a tradition, though a recent one, endeavoring to transmit itself unimpaired to posterity, but each instant losing some of its integrity? It has not the vitality and force of a single living man; for a single man can bend it to his will. It is a sort of wooden gun to the people themselves. But it is not the less necessary for this; for the people must have some complicated machinery or other, and hear its din, to satisfy that idea of government which they have. Governments show thus how successfully men can be imposed on, even impose on themselves, for their own advantage. It is excellent, we must all allow. Yet this government never of itself furthered any enterprise, but by the alacrity with which it got out of its way. *It* does not keep the country free. *It* does not settle the West. *It* does not educate. The character inherent in the American people has done all that has been accomplished; and it would have done somewhat more, if the government had not sometimes got in its way. For government is an expedient by which men would fain succeed in letting one another alone; and, as has been said, when it is most expedient, the governed are most let alone by it. Trade and commerce, if they were not made of India-rubber, would never manage to bounce over the obstacles which legislators are continually putting in their way; and, if one were to judge these men wholly by the effects of their actions and not partly by their intentions, they would deserve to be classed and punished with those mischievous persons who put obstructions on the railroads.

But, to speak practically and as a citizen, unlike those who call themselves no-government men, I ask for, not at once no government, but *at once* a better government. Let every man make known what kind of government would command his respect, and that will be one step toward obtaining it.

After all, the practical reason why, when the power is once in the hands of the people, a majority are permitted, and for a long period continue, to rule is not because they are most likely to be in the right, nor because this seems fairest to the minority, but because they are physically the strongest. But a government in which the majority rule in all cases cannot be based on justice, even as far as men understand it. Can there not be a government in which majorities do not virtually decide right and wrong, but conscience?—in which majorities decide only those questions to which the rule of expediency is applicable? Must the citizen ever for a moment, or in the least degree, resign his conscience to the legislator? Why has every man a conscience, then? I think that we should be men first, and subjects afterward. It is not desirable to cultivate a respect for the law, so much as for the right. The only obligation which I have a right to assume is to do at any time what I think right. It is truly enough said, that a corporation has no conscience; but a corporation of conscientious men is a corporation *with* a conscience. Law never made men a whit more just; and, by means of their respect for it, even the well-disposed are daily made the agents of injustice. A common and natural result of an undue respect for law is, that you may see a file of soldiers, colonel, captain, corporal, privates, powder-monkeys, and all, marching in admirable order over hill and dale to the wars, against their wills, ay, against their common sense and consciences, which makes it very steep marching indeed, and produces a palpitation of the heart. They have no doubt that it is a damnable business in which they are concerned; they are all peaceably inclined. Now, what are they? Men at all? or small movable forts and magazines, at the service of some unscrupulous man in power? Visit the Navy-Yard, and behold a marine, such a man as an American government can make, or such as it can make a man with its black arts—a mere shadow and reminiscence of humanity, a man laid out alive and standing, and already as one may say, buried under arms with funeral accompaniments, though it may be—

> Not a drum was heard, not a funeral note,
> As his corse to the rampart we hurried;
> Not a soldier discharged his farewell shot
> O'er the grave where our hero we buried.

The mass of men serve the state thus, not as men mainly, but as machines, with their bodies. They are the standing army, and the militia, jailors, constables, posse comitatus, etc. In most cases there is no free exercise whatever of the judgment or of the moral sense; but they put themselves on a level with wood and earth and stones; and wooden men can perhaps be manufactured that will serve the purpose as well. Such command no more respect than men of straw or a lump of dirt. They have the same sort of worth only as horses and dogs. Yet such as these even are commonly esteemed good citizens. Others—as most legislators, politicians, lawyers, ministers, and office-holders—serve the state chiefly with their heads; and, as they rarely make any moral distinctions, they are likely to serve the Devil, without *intending* it, as God. A very few, as heroes, patriots, martyrs, reformers in the great sense, and *men,* serve the state with their consciences also, and so necessarily resist it for the most part; and they are commonly treated as enemies by it. A wise man will only be useful as a man, and will not submit to be "clay," and "stop a hole to keep the wind away," but leave that office to his dust at least:

> I am too high-born to be propertied,
> To be a secondary at control,
> Or useful serving-man and instrument
> To any sovereign state throughout the world.

He who gives himself entirely to his fellow-men appears to them useless and selfish; but he who gives himself partially to them is pronounced a benefactor and philanthropist.

How does it become a man to behave toward this American government to-day? I answer, that he cannot without disgrace be associated with it. I cannot for an instant recognize that political organization as *my* government which is the *slave's* government also.

All men recognize the right of revolution; that is, the right to refuse allegiance to, and to resist, the government, when its tyranny or its inefficiency are great and unendurable. But almost all say that such is not the case now. But such was the case, they think, in the Revolution of '75. If one were to tell me that this was a bad government because it taxed certain foreign commodities brought to its ports, it is most probable that I should not make an ado about it, for I can do without them. All machines have their friction; and possibly this does enough good to counterbalance the evil. At any rate, it is a great evil to make a stir about it. But when the friction comes to have its machine, and oppression and robbery are organized, I say, let us not have such a machine any longer. In other words, when a sixth of the population of a nation which has undertaken to be the refuge of liberty are slaves, and a whole country is unjustly overrun and conquered by a foreign army, and subjected to military law, I think that it is not too soon for honest men to rebel and revolutionize. What makes this duty the more urgent is the fact that the country so overrun is not our own, but ours is the invading army.

Paley, a common authority with many on moral questions, in his chapter on the "Duty of Submission to Civil Government," resolves all civil obligation into expediency; and he proceeds to say, "that so long as the interest of the whole society requires it, that is, so long as the established government cannot be resisted or changed without public inconveniency, it is the will of God that the established government be obeyed, and no longer. . . . This principle being admitted, the justice of every particular case of resistance is reduced to a computation of the quantity of the danger and grievance on the one side, and of the probability and expense of redressing it on the other." Of this, he says, every man shall judge for himself. But Paley appears never to have contemplated those cases to which the rule of expediency does not apply, in which a people, as well as an individual, must do justice, cost what it may. If I have unjustly wrested a plank from a drowning man, I must restore it to him though I drown myself. This, according to Paley, would be inconvenient. But he that would save his life, in such a case, shall lose it. This people must cease to hold slaves, and to make war on Mexico, though it cost them their existence as a people.

In their practice, nations agree with Paley; but does any one think that Massachusetts does exactly what is right at the present crisis?

> A drab of state, a cloth-o'-silver slut,
> To have her train borne up, and her soul trail in the dirt.

Practically speaking, the opponents to a reform in Massachusetts are not a hundred thousand politicians at the South, but a hundred thousand merchants and farmers here, who are more interested in commerce and agriculture than they are in humanity, and are not prepared to do justice to the slave and to Mexico, *cost what it may*. I quarrel not with far-off foes, but with those who, near at home, co-operate with, and do the bidding of, those far away, and without whom the latter would be harmless. We are accustomed to say, that the mass of men are unprepared; but improvement is slow, because the few are not materially wiser or better than the many. It is not so important that many should be as good as you, as that there be some absolute goodness somewhere; for that will leaven the whole lump. There are thousands who are *in opinion* opposed to slavery and to the war, who yet in effect do nothing to put an end to them; who, esteeming themselves children of Washington and Franklin, sit down with their hands in their pockets, and say that they know not what to do, and do nothing; who even postpone the question of freedom to the question of free-trade, and quietly read the prices-current along with the latest advices from Mexico, after dinner, and, it may be, fall asleep over them both. What is the price-current of an honest man and patriot to-day? They hesitate, and they regret, and sometimes they petition; but they do nothing in earnest and with effect. They will wait, well disposed, for others to remedy the evil, that they may no longer have it to regret. At most, they give only a cheap vote, and a feeble countenance and God-speed, to the right, as it goes by them. There are nine hundred and ninety-nine patrons of virtue to one virtuous man. But it is easier to deal with the real possessor of a thing than with the temporary guardian of it.

All voting is a sort of gaming, like checkers or backgammon, with a slight moral tinge to it, a playing with right and wrong, with moral questions; and betting naturally accompanies it. The character of the voters is not staked. I cast my vote, perchance, as I think right; but I am not vitally concerned that that right should prevail. I am willing to leave it to the majority. Its obligation, therefore, never exceeds that of expediency. Even voting *for the right* is *doing* nothing for it. It is only expressing to men feebly your desire that it should prevail. A wise man will not leave the right to the mercy of chance, nor wish it to prevail through the power of the majority. There is but little virtue in the action of masses of men. When the majority shall at length vote for the abolition of slavery, it will be because they are indifferent to slavery, or because there is but little slavery left to be abolished by their vote. *They* will then be the only slaves. Only *his* vote can hasten the abolition of slavery who asserts his own freedom by his vote.

I hear of a convention to be held at Baltimore, or elsewhere, for the selection of a candidate for the Presidency, made up chiefly of editors, and men who are politicians by profession; but I think, what is it to any independent, intelligent, and respectable man what decision they may come to? Shall we not have the advantage of his wisdom and honesty, nevertheless? Can we not count upon some independent votes? Are there not many individuals in the country who do not attend conventions? But no: I find that the respectable man, so called, has immediately drifted from his position, and despairs of his country, when his country has more reason to despair of him. He forthwith adopts one of the candidates thus selected as the only *available* one, thus proving that he is himself *available* for any purposes of the demagogue. His vote is of no more worth than that of any unprincipled foreigner or hireling native, who may have been bought. O for a man who is a *man,* and, as my neighbor says, has a bone in his back which you cannot pass your hand through! Our statistics are at fault: the population has been returned too large. How many *men* are there to a square thousand miles in this country? Hardly one. Does not America offer any inducement for men to settle here? The American has dwindled into an Odd Fellow—one who may be known by the development of his organ of gregariousness, and a manifest lack of intellect and cheerful self-reliance; whose first and chief concern, on coming into the world, is to see that the Almshouses are in good repair; and, before yet he has lawfully donned the virile garb, to collect a fund for the support of the widows and orphans that may be; who, in short, ventures to live only by the aid of the Mutual Insurance company, which has promised to bury him decently.

It is not a man's duty, as a matter of course, to devote himself to the eradication of any, even the most enormous wrong; he may still properly have other concerns to engage him; but it is his duty, at least, to wash his hands of it, and, if he gives it no thought longer, not to give it practically his support. If I devote myself to other pursuits and contemplations, I must first see, at least, that I do not pursue them sitting upon another man's shoulders. I must get off him first, that he may pursue his contemplations too. See what gross inconsistency is tolerated. I have heard some of my townsmen say, "I should like to have them order me out to help put down an insurrection of the slaves, or to march to Mexico—see if I would go"; and yet these very men have each, directly by their allegiance, and so indirectly, at least, by their money, furnished a substitute. The soldier is applauded who refuses to serve in an unjust war by those who do not refuse to sustain the unjust government which makes the war; is applauded by those whose own act and authority he disregards and sets at naught; as if the state were penitent to that degree that it hired one to scourge it while it sinned, but not to that degree that it left off sinning for a moment. Thus, under the name of Order and Civil Government, we are all made at last to pay homage to and support our own meanness. After the first blush of sin comes its indifference; and from immoral it becomes, as it were, *un*moral, and not quite unnecessary to that life which we have made.

The broadest and most prevalent error requires the most disinterested virtue to sustain it. The slight reproach to which the virtue of patriotism is commonly liable, the noble are most likely to incur. Those who, while they disapprove of the character and measures of a government, yield to it their allegiance and support are undoubtedly its most conscientious supporters, and so frequently the most serious obstacles to reform. Some are petitioning the state to dissolve the Union, to disregard the requisitions of the President. Why do they not dissolve it themselves—the union between themselves and the state—and refuse to pay their quota into its treasury? Do not they stand in the same relation to the state that the state does to the Union? And have not the same reasons prevented the state from resisting the Union which have prevented them from resisting the state?

How can a man be satisfied to entertain an opinion merely, and enjoy *it?* Is there any enjoyment in it, if his opinion is that he is aggrieved? If you are cheated out of a single dollar by your neighbor, you do not rest satisfied with knowing that you are cheated, or with saying that you are cheated, or even with petitioning him to pay you your due; but you take effectual steps at once to obtain the full amount, and see that you are never cheated again. Action from principle, the perception and the performance of right, changes things and relations; it is essentially revolutionary, and does not consist wholly with anything which was. It not only divides states and churches, it divides families; ay, it divides the *individual,* separating the diabolical in him from the divine.

Unjust laws exist: shall we be content to obey them, or shall we endeavor to amend them, and obey them until we have succeeded, or shall we transgress them at once? Men generally, under such a government as this, think that they ought to wait until they have persuaded the majority to alter them. They think that, if they should resist, the remedy would be worse than the evil. But it is the fault of the government itself that the remedy *is* worse than the evil. *It* makes it worse. Why is it not more apt to anticipate and provide for reform? Why does it not cherish its wise minority? Why does it cry and resist before it is hurt? Why does it not encourage its citizens to be on the alert to point out its faults, and *do* better than it would have them? Why does it always crucify Christ, and excommunicate Copernicus and Luther, and pronounce Washington and Franklin rebels?

One would think that a deliberate and practical denial of its authority was the only offense never contemplated by government; else, why has it not assigned its definite, its suitable and proportionate penalty? If a man who has no property refuses but once to earn nine shillings for the state, he is put in prison for a period unlimited by any law that I know, and determined only by the discretion of those who placed him there; but if he should steal ninety times nine shillings from the state, he is soon permitted to go at large again.

If the injustice is part of the necessary friction of the machine of government, let it go, let it go: perchance it will wear smooth—certainly the machine will wear out. If the injustice has a spring, or a pulley, or a rope, or a crank, exclusively for itself, then perhaps you may consider whether the remedy will not be worse than the evil; but if it is of such a nature that it requires you to be the agent of injustice to another, then, I say, break the law. Let your life be a counter friction to stop the machine. What I have to do is to see, at any rate, that I do not lend myself to the wrong which I condemn.

As for adopting the ways which the state has provided for remedying the evil, I know not of such ways. They take too much time, and a man's life will be gone. I have other affairs to attend to. I came into this world, not chiefly to make this a good place to live in, but to live in it, be it good or bad. A man has not everything to do, but something; and because he cannot do *everything*, it is not necessary that he should do *something* wrong. It is not my business to be petitioning the Governor or the Legislature any more than it is theirs to petition me; and if they should not hear my petition, what should I do then? But in this case the state has provided no way: its very Constitution is the evil. This may seem to be harsh and stubborn and unconciliatory; but it is to treat with the utmost kindness and consideration the only spirit that can appreciate or deserves it. So is all change for the better, like birth and death, which convulse the body.

I do not hesitate to say, that those who call themselves Abolitionists should at once effectually withdraw their support, both in person and property, from the government of Massachusetts and not wait till they constitute a majority of one, before they suffer the right to prevail through them. I think that it is enough if they have God on their side, without waiting for that other one. Moreover, any man more right than his neighbors constitutes a majority of one already.

I meet this American government, or its representative, the state government, directly, and face to face, once a year—no more—in the person of its tax-gatherer; this is the only mode in which a man situated as I am necessarily meets it; and it then says distinctly, Recognize me; and the simplest, most effectual, and, in the present posture of affairs, the indispensablest mode of treating with it on this head, of expressing your little satisfaction with and love for it, is to deny it then. My civil neighbor, the tax-gatherer, is the very man I have to deal with—for it is, after all, with men and not with parchment that I quarrel—and he has voluntarily chosen to be an agent of the government. How shall he ever know well what he is and does

as an officer of the government, or as a man, until he is obliged
to consider whether he shall treat me, his neighbor, for whom
he has respect, as a neighbor and well-disposed man, or as a
maniac and disturber of the peace, and see if he can get over
this obstruction to his neighborliness without a ruder and more
impetuous thought or speech corresponding with his action. I
know this well, that if one thousand, if one hundred, if ten
men whom I could name—if ten *honest* men only—ay, if *one*
HONEST man, in this State of Massachusetts, *ceasing to hold
slaves,* were actually to withdraw from this co-partnership, and
be locked up in the county jail therefor, it would be the abolition
of slavery in America. For it matters not how small the beginning
may seem to be: what is once well done is done forever. But
we love better to talk about it: that we say is our mission.
Reform keeps many scores of newspapers in its service, but not
one man. If my esteemed neighbor, the State's ambassador, who
will devote his days to the settlement of the question of human
rights in the Council Chamber, instead of being threatened with
the prisons of Carolina, were to sit down the prisoner of Massachusetts, that State which is so anxious to foist the sin of
slavery upon her sister—though at present she can discover only
an act of inhospitality to be the ground of a quarrel with her
—the Legislature would not wholly waive the subject the following winter.

Under a government which imprisons any unjustly, the true
place for a just man is also a prison. The proper place to-day,
the only place which Massachusetts has provided for her freer
and less desponding spirits, is in her prisons, to be put out and
locked out of the State by her own act, as they have already
put themselves out by their principles. It is there that the fugitive
slave, and the Mexican prisoner on parole, and the Indian come
to plead the wrongs of his race should find them; on that separate, but more free and honorable ground, where the State
places those who are not *with* her, but *against* her—the only

house in a slave State in which a free man can abide with honor. If any think that their influence would be lost there, and their voices no longer afflict the ear of the State, that they would not be as an enemy within its walls, they do not know by how much truth is stronger than error, nor how much more eloquently and effectively he can combat injustice who has experienced a little in his own person. Cast your whole vote, not a strip of paper merely, but your whole influence. A minority is powerless while it conforms to the majority; it is not even a minority then; but it is irresistible when it clogs by its whole weight. If the alternative is to keep all just men in prison, or give up war and slavery, the State will not hesitate which to choose. If a thousand men were not to pay their tax-bills this year, that would not be a violent and bloody measure, as it would be to pay them, and enable the State to commit violence and shed innocent blood. This is, in fact, the definition of a peaceable revolution, if any such is possible. If the tax-gatherer, or any other public officer, asks me, as one has done, "But what shall I do?" my answer is, "If you really wish to do anything, resign your office." When the subject has refused allegiance, and the officer has resigned his office, then the revolution is accomplished. But even suppose blood should flow. Is there not a sort of blood shed when the conscience is wounded? Through this wound a man's real manhood and immortality flow out, and he bleeds to an everlasting death. I see this blood flowing now.

I have contemplated the imprisonment of the offender, rather than the seizure of his goods—though both will serve the same purpose—because they who assert the purest right, and consequently are most dangerous to a corrupt State, commonly have not spent much time in accumulating property. To such the State renders comparatively small service, and a slight tax is wont to appear exorbitant, particularly if they are obliged to earn it by special labor with their hands. If there were one who lived wholly without the use of money, the State itself would hesitate to demand it of him. But the rich man—not to make any invidious comparison—is always sold to the institution which makes him rich. Absolutely speaking, the more money, the less virtue; for money comes between a man and his objects, and obtains them for him; and it was certainly no great virtue to obtain it. It puts to rest many questions which he would otherwise be taxed to answer; while the only new question which it puts is the hard but superfluous one, how to spend it. Thus his moral ground is taken from under his feet. The opportunities of living are diminished in proportion as what are called the "means" are increased. The best thing a man can do for his culture when he is rich is to endeavor to carry out those schemes which he entertained when he was poor. Christ answered the Herodians according to their condition. "Show me the tribute-money," said he; and one took a penny out of his pocket; if you use money which has the image of Caesar on it and which he has made current and valuable, that is, *if you are men of the State,* and gladly enjoy the advantages of Caesar's government, then pay him back some of his own when he demands it. "Render therefore to Caesar that which is Caesar's, and to God those things which are God's"—leaving them no wiser than before as to which was which; for they did not wish to know.

When I converse with the freest of my neighbors, I perceive that, whatever they may say about the magnitude and seriousness of the question, and their regard for the public tranquillity, the long and the short of the matter is, that they cannot spare the protection of the existing government, and they dread the consequences to their property and families of disobedience to it. For my own part, I should not like to think that I ever rely on the protection of the State. But, if I deny the authority of the State when it presents its tax-bill, it will soon take and waste all my property, and so harass me and my children without end. This is hard. This makes it impossible for a man to live honestly, and at the same time comfortably, in outward respects. It will not be worth the while to accumulate property; that would be sure to go again. You must hire or squat somewhere, and raise but a small crop, and eat that soon. You must live within yourself, and depend upon yourself always tucked up and ready for a start, and not have many affairs. A man may grow rich in Turkey even, if he will be in all respects a good subject of the Turkish government. Confucius said: "If a state is governed by the principles of reason, poverty and misery are subjects of shame; if a state is not governed by the principles of reason, riches and honors are the subjects of shame." No: until I want the protection of Massachusetts to be extended to me in some distant Southern port, where my liberty is endangered, or until I am bent solely on building up an estate at home by peaceful enterprise, I can afford to refuse allegiance to Massachusetts, and her right to my property and life. It costs me less in every sense to incur the penalty of disobedience to the State than it would to obey. I should feel as if I were worth less in that case.

Some years ago, the State met me in behalf of the Church, and commanded me to pay a certain sum toward the support of a clergyman whose preaching my father attended, but never I myself. "Pay," it said, "or be locked up in the jail." I declined to pay, but, unfortunately, another man saw fit to pay it. I did not see why the schoolmaster should be taxed to support the priest, and not the priest the schoolmaster; for I was not the State's schoolmaster, but I supported myself by voluntary subscription. I did not see why the lyceum should not present its tax-bill, and have the State to back its demand, as well as the Church. However, at the request of the selectmen, I condescended to make some such statement as this in writing: "Know all men by these presents, that I, Henry Thoreau, do not wish to be regarded as a member of any incorporated society which I have not joined." This I gave to the town clerk; and he has it. The State, having thus learned that I did not wish to be regarded as a member of that church, has never made a like demand on me since; though it said that it must adhere to its original presumption that time. If I had known how to name them, I should then have signed off in detail from all the societies which I never signed on to; but I did not know where to find a complete list.

I have paid no poll-tax for six years. I was put into a jail once on this account, for one night; and, as I stood considering the walls of solid stone, two or three feet thick, the door of wood and iron, a foot thick, and the iron grating which strained the light, I could not help being struck with the foolishness of that institution which treated me as if I were mere flesh and blood and bones, to be locked up. I wondered that it should have concluded at length that this was the best use it could put me to, and had never thought to avail itself of my services in some way. I saw that, if there was a wall of stone between me and my townsmen, there was a still more difficult one to climb or break through before they could get to be as free as I was. I did not for a moment feel confined, and the walls seemed a great waste of stone and mortar. I felt as if I alone of all my townsmen had paid my tax. They plainly did not know how to treat me, but behaved like persons who are underbred. In every threat and in every compliment there was a blunder; for they thought that my chief desire was to stand the other side of the stone wall. I could not but smile to see how industriously they locked the door on my meditations, which followed them out again without let or hindrance, and *they* were really all that was dangerous. As they could not reach me, they had resolved to punish my body; just as boys, if they cannot come at some person against whom they have a spite, will abuse his dog. I saw that the State was half-witted, and it was timid as a lone woman with her silver spoons, and that it did not know its friends from its foes, and I lost all my remaining respect for it, and pitied it.

Thus the State never intentionally confronts a man's sense, intellectual or moral, but only his body, his senses. It is not armed with superior wit or honesty, but with superior physical strength. I was not born to be forced. I will breathe after my own fashion. Let us see who is the strongest. What force has a multitude? They only can force me who obey a higher law than I. They force me to become like themselves. I do not hear of *men* being *forced* to live this way or that by masses of men. What sort of life were that to live? When I meet a government which says to me, "Your money or your life," why should I be in haste to give it my money? It may be in a great strait, and not know what to do: I cannot help that. It must help itself; do as I do. It is not worth the while to snivel about it. I am not responsible for the successful working of the machinery of society. I am not the son of the engineer. I perceive that, when an acorn and a chestnut fall side by side, the one does not remain inert to make way for the other, but both obey their own laws, and spring and grow and flourish as best they can, till one, perchance, overshadows and destroys the other. If a plant cannot live according to its nature, it dies; and so a man.

The night in prison was novel and interesting enough. The prisoners in their shirt-sleeves were enjoying a chat and the evening air in the doorway, when I entered. But the jailer said, "Come, boys, it is time to lock up"; and so they dispersed, and I heard the sound of their steps returning into the hollow apartments. My room-mate was introduced to me by the jailer as "a first-rate fellow and a clever man." When the door was locked, he showed me where to hang my hat, and how he managed matters there. The rooms were whitewashed once a month; and this one, at least, was the whitest, most simply furnished, and probably the neatest apartment in the town. He naturally wanted to know where I came from, and what brought me there; and, when I had told him, I asked him in my turn how he came there, presuming him to be an honest man, of course; and, as the world goes, I believe he was. "Why," said he, "they accuse me of burning a barn; but I never did it." As near as I could discover, he had probably gone to bed in a barn when drunk, and smoked his pipe there; and so a barn was burnt. He had the reputation of being a clever man, had been there some three months waiting for his trial to come on, and would have to wait as much longer; but he was quite domesticated and contented, since he got his board for nothing, and thought that he was well treated.

He occupied one window, and I the other; and I saw that if one stayed there long, his principal business would be to look out the window. I had soon read all the tracts that were left there, and examined where former prisoners had broken out, and where a grate had been sawed off, and heard the history of the various occupants of that room; for I found that even here there was a history and a gossip which never circulated beyond the walls of the jail. Probably this is the only house in the town where verses are composed, which are afterward printed in a circular form, but not published. I was shown quite a long list of verses which were composed by some young men who had been detected in an attempt to escape, who avenged themselves by singing them.

I pumped my fellow-prisoner as dry as I could, for fear I should never see him again; but at length he showed me which was my bed, and left me to blow out the lamp.

It was like traveling into a far country, such as I had never expected to behold, to lie there for one night. It seemed to me that I never had heard the town-clock strike before, nor the evening sounds of the village; for we slept with the windows open, which were inside the grating. It was to see my native village in the light of the Middle Ages, and our Concord was turned into a Rhine stream, and visions of knights and castles passed before me. They were the voices of old burghers that I heard in the streets. I was an involuntary spectator and auditor of whatever was done and said in the kitchen of the adjacent village-inn—a wholly new and rare experience to me. It was a closer view of my native town. I was fairly inside of it. I never had seen its institutions before. This is one of its peculiar institutions; for it is a shire town. I began to comprehend what its inhabitants were about.

In the morning, our breakfasts were put through the hole in the door, in small oblong-square tin pans, made to fit, and holding a pint of chocolate, with brown bread, and an iron spoon. When they called for the vessels again, I was green enough to return what bread I had left; but my comrade seized it, and said that I should lay that up for lunch or dinner. Soon after he was let out to work at haying in a neighboring field, whither he went every day, and would not be back till noon; so he bade me good-day, saying that he doubted if he should see me again.

When I came out of prison—for some one interfered, and paid that tax—I did not perceive that great changes had taken place on the common, such as he observed who went in a youth and emerged a tottering and gray-headed man; and yet a change had to my eyes come over the scene—the town, and State, and country—greater than any that mere time could effect. I saw yet more distinctly the State in which I lived. I saw to what extent the people among whom I lived could be trusted as good neighbors and friends; that their friendship was for summer weather only; that they did not greatly propose to do right; that they were a distinct race from me by their prejudices and superstitions, as the Chinamen and Malays are; that in their sacrifices to humanity they ran no risks, not even to their property; that after all they were not so noble but they treated the thief as he had treated them, and hoped, by a certain outward observance and a few prayers, and by walking in a particular straight though useless path from time to time, to save their souls. This may be to judge my neighbors harshly; for I believe that many of them are not aware that they have such an institution as the jail in their village.

It was formerly the custom in our village, when a poor debtor came out of jail, for his acquaintances to salute him, looking through their fingers, which were crossed to represent the grating of a jail window, "How do ye do?" My neighbors did not thus salute me, but first looked at me, and then at one another, as if I had returned from a long journey. I was put into jail as I was going to the shoemaker's to get a shoe which was mended. When I was let out the next morning, I proceeded to finish my errand, and, having put on my mended shoe, joined a huckleberry party, who were impatient to put themselves under my conduct; and in half an hour—for the horse was soon tackled —was in the midst of a huckleberry field, on one of our highest hills, two miles off, and then the State was nowhere to be seen. This is the whole history of "My Prisons."

I have never declined paying the highway tax, because I am as desirous of being a good neighbor as I am of being a bad subject; and as for supporting schools, I am doing my part to educate my fellow-countrymen now. It is for no particular item in the tax-bill that I refuse to pay it. I simply wish to refuse allegiance to the State, to withdraw and stand aloof from it effectually. I do not care to trace the course of my dollar, if I could, till it buys a man or a musket to shoot with—the dollar is innocent —but I am concerned to trace the effects of my allegiance. In fact, I quietly declare war with the State, after my fashion, though I will still make what use and get what advantage of her I can, as is usual in such cases.

If others pay the tax which is demanded of me, from a sympathy with the State, they do but what they have already done in their own case, or rather they abet injustice to a greater extent than the State requires. If they pay the tax from a mistaken interest in the individual taxed, to save his property, or prevent his going to jail, it is because they have not considered wisely how far they let their private feelings interfere with the public good.

This, then, is my position at present. But one cannot be too much on his guard in such a case, lest his action be biased by obstinacy or an undue regard for the opinions of men. Let him see that he does only what belongs to himself and to the hour.

I think sometimes, Why, this people mean well, they are only ignorant; they would do better if they knew how: why give your neighbors this pain to treat you as they are not inclined to? But I think again, This is no reason why I should do as they do, or permit others to suffer much greater pain of a different kind. Again, I sometimes say to myself, When many millions of men, without heat, without ill will, without personal feeling of any kind, demand of you a few shillings only, without the possibility, such is their constitution, of retracting or altering their present demand, and without the possibility, on your side, of appeal to any other millions, why expose yourself to this overwhelming brute force? You do not resist cold and hunger, the winds and the waves, thus obstinately; you quietly submit to a thousand similar necessities. You do not put your head into the fire. But just in proportion as I regard this as not wholly a brute force, but partly a human force, and consider that I have relations to those millions as to so many millions of men, and not of mere brute or inanimate things, I see that appeal is possible, first and instantaneously, from them to the Maker of them, and, secondly, from them to themselves. But if I put my head deliberately into the fire, there is no appeal to fire or to the Maker of fire, and I have only myself to blame. If I could convince myself that I have any right to be satisfied with men as they are, and to treat them accordingly, and not according, in some respects, to my requisitions and expectations of what they and I ought to be, then, like a good Mussulman and fatalist, I should endeavor to be satisfied with things as they are, and say it is the will of God. And, above all, there is this difference between resisting this and a purely brute or natural force, that I can resist this with some effect; but I cannot expect, like Orpheus, to change the nature of the rocks and trees and beasts.

I do not wish to quarrel with any man or nation. I do not wish to split hairs, to make fine distinctions, or set myself up as better than my neighbors. I seek rather, I may say, even an excuse for conforming to the laws of the land. I am but too ready to conform to them. Indeed, I have reason to suspect myself on this head; and each year, as the tax-gatherer comes round, I find myself disposed to review the acts and position of the general and State governments, and the spirit of the people, to discover a pretext for conformity.

> We must affect our country as our parents,
> And if at any time we alienate
> Our love or industry from doing it honor,
> We must respect effects and teach the soul
> Matter of conscience and religion,
> And not desire of rule or benefit.

I believe that the State will soon be able to take all my work of this sort out of my hands, and then I shall be no better a patriot than my fellow-countrymen. Seen from a lower point of view, the Constitution, with all its faults, is very good; the law and the courts are very respectable; even this State and this American government are, in many respects, very admirable, and rare things, to be thankful for, such as a great many have described them; but seen from a point of view a little higher, they are what I have described them; seen from a higher still, and the highest, who shall say what they are, or that they are worth looking at or thinking of at all?

However, the government does not concern me much, and I shall bestow the fewest possible thoughts on it. It is not many moments that I live under a government, even in this world. If a man is thought-free, fancy-free, imagination-free, that which *is not* never for a long time appearing *to be* to him, unwise rulers or reformers cannot fatally interrupt him.

I know that most men think differently from myself; but those whose lives are by profession devoted to the study of these or kindred subjects content me as little as any. Statesmen and legislators, standing so completely within the institution, never distinctly and nakedly behold it. They speak of moving society, but have no resting-place without it. They may be men of a certain experience and discrimination, and have no doubt invented ingenious and even useful systems, for which we sincerely thank them; but all their wit and usefulness lie within certain not very wide limits. They are wont to forget that the world is not governed by policy and expediency. Webster never goes behind government, and so cannot speak with authority about it. His words are wisdom to those legislators who contemplate no essential reform in the existing government; but for thinkers, and those who legislate for all time, he never once glances at the subject. I know of those whose serene and wise speculations on this theme would soon reveal the limits of his mind's range and hospitality. Yet, compared with the cheap professions of most reformers, and the still cheaper wisdom and eloquence of politicians in general, his are almost the only sensible and valuable words, and we thank Heaven for him. Comparatively, he is always strong, original, and, above all, practical. Still, his quality is not wisdom, but prudence. The lawyer's truth is not Truth, but consistency or a consistent expediency. Truth is always in harmony with herself, and is not concerned chiefly to reveal the justice that may consist with wrong-doing. He well deserves to be called, as he has been called, the Defender of the Constitution. There are really no blows to be given by him but defensive ones. He is not a leader, but a follower. His leaders are the men of '87. "I have never made an effort," he says, "and never propose to make an effort; I have never countenanced an effort, and never mean to countenance an effort, to disturb the arrangement as originally made, by which the various States came into the Union." Still thinking of the sanction which the Constitution gives to slavery, he says, "Because it was a part of the original compact—let it stand." Notwithstanding his special acuteness and ability, he is unable to take a fact out of its merely political relations, and behold it as it lies absolutely to be disposed of by the intellect—what, for instance, it behooves a man to do here in America to-day with regard to slavery—but ventures, or is driven, to make some such desperate answer as the following, while professing to speak absolutely, and as a private man—from which what new and singular code of social duties might be inferred? "The manner," says he, "in which the governments of those States where slavery exists are to regulate it is for their own consideration, under their responsibility to their constituents, to the general laws of propriety, humanity, and justice, and to God. Associations formed elsewhere, springing from a feeling of humanity, or other cause, have nothing whatever to do with it. They have never received any encouragement from me, and they never will."

They who know of no purer sources of truth, who have traced up its stream no higher, stand, and wisely stand, by the Bible and the Constitution, and drink at it there with reverence and humility; but they who behold where it comes trickling into this lake or that pool, gird up their loins once more, and continue their pilgrimage toward its fountain-head.

No man with a genius for legislation has appeared in America. They are rare in the history of the world. There are orators, politicians, and eloquent men, by the thousand; but the speaker has not yet opened his mouth to speak who is capable of settling the much-vexed questions of the day. We love eloquence for its own sake, and not for any truth which it may utter, or any heroism it may inspire. Our legislators have not yet learned the comparative value of free-trade and of freedom, of union, and of rectitude, to a nation. They have no genius or talent for comparatively humble questions of taxation and finance, commerce and manufactures and agriculture. If we were left solely to the wordy wit of legislators in Congress for our guidance, uncorrected by the seasonable experience and the effectual complaints of the people, America would not long retain her rank among the nations. For eighteen hundred years, though perchance I have no right to say it, the New Testament has been written; yet where is the legislator who has wisdom and practical talent enough to avail himself of the light which it sheds on the science of legislation?

The authority of government, even such as I am willing to submit to—for I will cheerfully obey those who know and can do better than I, and in many things even those who neither know nor can do so well—is still an impure one: to be strictly just, it must have the sanction and consent of the governed. It can have no pure right over my person and property but what I concede to it. The progress from an absolute to a limited monarchy, from a limited monarchy to a democracy, is a progress toward a true respect for the individual. Even the Chinese philosopher was wise enough to regard the individual as the basis of the empire. Is a democracy, such as we know it, the last improvement possible in government? Is it not possible to take a step further toward recognizing and organizing the rights of man? There will never be a really free and enlightened State until the State comes to recognize the individual as a higher and independent power, from which all its own power and authority are derived, and treats him accordingly. I please myself with imagining a State at last which can afford to be just to all men, and to treat the individual with respect as a neighbor; which even would not think it inconsistent with its own repose if a few were to live aloof from it, not meddling with it, nor embraced by it, who fulfilled all the duties of neighbors and fellow-men. A State which bore this kind of fruit, and suffered it to drop off as fast as it ripened, would prepare the way for a still more perfect and glorious State, which also I have imagined, but not yet anywhere seen.